1986

Nuclear Winter

The Evidence and the Risks

Owen Greene, Ian Percival and Irene Ridge

Polity Press

First published 1985 by Polity Press, Cambridge, in association with Basil Blackwell, Oxford. Reprinted 1985.

Editorial Office: Polity Press, Dales Brewery, Gwydir Street, Cambridge CB1 2LJ.

Basil Blackwell Ltd
108, Cowley Road, Oxford OX4 1JF, UK.

Basil Blackwell Inc.
432 Park Avenue South, Suite 1505, New York, NY 10016, USA.

British Library Cataloguing in Publication Data

Greene, Owen
 Nuclear winter: the evidence and risks.
 1. Nuclear warfare — Environmental aspects
 I. Title   II. Percival, Ian, 1931–
 III. Ridge, Irene
 574.5'222   QH545.N83

ISBN 7456–0176–6
ISBN 0–7456–0177–4 Pbk

Library of Congress Cataloging in Publication Data

Greene, Owen.
 Nuclear Winter.
 Bibliography: p.
 Includes index.
 1. Nuclear warfare — Environmental aspects —
Addresses, essays, lectures. I. Percival, Ian,
1931– . II. Ridge, Irene. III. Title.
U263.G74 1985 574.5'222 85–9458

ISBN 0–7456–0176–6
ISBN 0–7456–0177–4 (pbk.)

Typeset by Oxford Publishing Services, Oxford
Printed in Great Britain by
Whitstable Litho Ltd., Whitstable, Kent

Contents

For Barbara, Jill and John

Acknowledgements

We are very grateful to all of the many people who provided us with information and advice on all the subjects covered in this book. In particular, we want to thank Peter Gahan, Bob Harwood and Alan Longman who prepared information specifically for this book and Paul Crutzen, Dougal Drysdale, Mick Kelly, Norman Myers, Richard Turco and Jacob Sheer who provided us with much valuable material. Thanks are also due to Bruce Atkinson, John Beckman, Michael Berry, Shaun Bullett, John Clarke, Marianne Fillenz, Michael Hoare, Mick Jackson, Chris Meredith, Mitchell Moncrieff, George Mulholland, Barbara Pearce, Mike Pentz, S. Rasbash, Derek Richards, Helen Richards, Michael Rowan-Robinson, Carl Sagan, Keith Shine, Jonathan Silvertown, Stuart Simons, Steve Soter, Philip Steadman, Philip Webber and Graeme Wilkinson for reading and commenting on sections of the text and for other help. The staff of Polity Press and Basil Blackwell, particularly Tony Giddens, Michael Hay, Sue Miller and Helen Pilgrim, worked hard, prepared the book for press, and provided many valuable suggestions and we are very grateful to them for it. We benefited greatly from our contact with the many scientists involved in the ongoing SCOPE–ENUWAR inquiry into the environmental consequences of nuclear war, though the inquiry continues and this book in no way prejudices its con-

Acknowledgements

clusions. People who wish to know these, and the results of research prepared for the inquiry will have to await the SCOPE report. Finally we thank all of our colleagues in Scientists Against Nuclear Arms (SANA) who have provided stimulating discussion and advice on the topic covered in this book. As always, however, the final responsibility for the contents of this book is ours alone. The authors and publisher would like to thank the individuals, institutions and publishing houses who granted permission to reproduce previously published material in this book. Full details of all such material are given in the notes (p.202).

Note on Reading Nuclear Winter

In this book there are 'boxes' in the text and appendices at the back of the book that give more detailed information or scientific data. These are not necessary to the main thread of the discussion and many readers may prefer to skip them and return to them later.

Units

In any book of this kind, tricky decisions about units have to be made. The units with which members of the public are most familiar (for example, miles and pounds) are often not the ones that are used within the scientific community (such as kilometers, kilograms, and metric tonnes). Furthermore, the subject matter cuts across a number of disciplines, which use a variety of systems of units. Sometimes, for historical reasons, these can be a strange mixture of British Imperial, SI and cgs units. This confusion is unfortunate, but it must be lived with until the disciplines reform themselves.

In the body of the text we have stuck to the most widely understood units. Where appropriate the values in the 'correct' units are given in brackets so that readers who are more familiar with the topic can easily compare our assumptions with those of other people. In the appendices and the more technical of the boxes and figures, we use the units typical to the given discipline. General readers need not be unnerved by this. The qualitative information in these more technical sections should be clear, and in any case such sections can be omitted without losing the thread of the discussion.

The conversion factors for some of more common quantities are listed below.

1 kilometer (km)	0.62 miles	
1 square kilometer (sq km)	0.39 square miles (sq mi)	
1 meter (m)	100 centimeters (cm)	1.1 yards
1 tonne (metric tonne)	1,000 kilograms (kg)	0.98 tons
1 calorie (cal)	4.186 joules (J)	
1 megawatt (MW)	1,000,000 watts (W)	1,341 horsepower
1 pound per square inch (psi)	6,895 pascal	
0 degrees Centigrade (°C)	0 degrees Celsius	32 degrees Farhenheit

The unit 'rads' is referred to regularly in the book: it is a unit of radiation dose to living tissues.

1 Introduction

Immense resources have been devoted to the design of nuclear weapons, but relatively few to studies of the drastic impact on our environment of using these in war.

A very important contribution to these studies was commissioned by the editors of *Ambio*, the environmental journal of the Royal Swedish Academy of Sciences, and published in November 1982. It sparked off an ominous line of enquiry which showed that our whole environment is at risk.

The key new factor was discovered by accident. The *Ambio* editors asked Dutch scientist Paul Crutzen and his American colleague John Birks to investigate the effects of nuclear war on the atmosphere, thinking that they would concentrate, as many others had done, on studying the increased amounts of dangerous ultraviolet radiation that would reach the Earth's surface.

But it occurred to them that smoke from fires ignited by the heat of the nuclear fireballs could affect the issue, so they made some rough calculations, and, to their astonishment, found that there could be enough smoke to blot out nearly all of the sunlight from half the Earth for weeks on end.[1] The key factor that scientists had neglected for over thirty years was smoke!

There could be twilight at noon.

This discovery helped to stimulate many other scientists

to further research, including five Americans with international reputations in the atmospheric and planetary sciences. Their names were Turco, Toon, Ackerman, Pollack and Sagan — TTAPS for convenience. They made .more detailed calculations, and they found that summer could be turned into winter in a week or two.[2]

There could be a nuclear winter.

The TTAPS scientists decided that these surprising results should be thoroughly checked, and they asked dozens of eminent scientists to examine their work. They presented their results at a meeting in Cambridge, Massachusetts, which was attended by many biologists. These included Professor Paul Ehrlich of Stanford University, who assembled a large group of distinguished biologists and ecologists to find out what might happen to plants and animals.[3] They concluded that in a large scale nuclear war many plant and animal species could be made extinct.

The extinction of the human race could not be ruled out.

The results of TTAPS, the biologists and other American and Soviet scientists were announced at a Washington meeting in late 1983.[4]

There have now been extensive studies by a large number of different groups, and there is reasonable agreement between them on the probable major global effects of a large-scale nuclear war. These were summarized in early 1985 in a report by a Committee of the National Research Council of the most senior scientific organization in the USA: the US National Academy of Sciences. This is the 'NRC Report'.[5]

In 1983, the International Council of Scientific Unions set up the ENUWAR steering committee on the environmental consequences of nuclear war, which has been coordinating international research on a very wide scale, and is due to report in the late Summer of 1985.[6] The

Royal Society of Canada published a detailed assessment of research into the nuclear winter and its effects in early 1985.[7]

Currently available scientific evidence indicates that a large-scale nuclear war would be followed by a bigger change in the climate of the Earth for at least several months, than at any time in recorded history, and probably since humans first walked the Earth. The closest comparisons are with dust storms on Mars and with possible environmental catastrophes millions of years ago that might have helped to wipe out dinosaurs and other species.

These are the likely costs of nuclear war.

In this book we describe what could happen and how. The scientific details are complicated, but we concentrate on the basic processes, which are relatively easy to understand. In the final two chapters we discuss the implications for policy and for the future.

The effects of nuclear war

Here is a summary of the principal effects that would be expected if a significant fraction of the world's nuclear arsenals were used in war.

1 Nuclear explosions would send dust, radioactivity and various gases into the atmosphere.
2 The explosions would ignite fires, burning cities, forests, fuel and grasslands in the countries of the nuclear alliances. The total area they covered would probably be several times greater than that of the United Kingdom.
3 The fires would send plumes of smoke and gases tens of thousands of feet into the atmosphere.
4 Within a week or two, some of the dust, radioactivity

and smoke would be carried by the wind around the Earth. It might stay in the atmosphere for days, months or even years, depending on its height.

5 In a week or two, clouds of smoke and dust would spread around the Earth mainly in a zone from Texas in the south to the north of Norway. Then it would spread further to the north and south, possibly across the equator. In weeks or possibly months it would settle slowly to the ground.

6 Under the cloud of smoke and dust, daylight could be reduced to near darkness for days and to twilight for weeks.

7 Temperatures would drop on land under the clouds of smoke and dust. Particularly after a spring or summer war, these temperature reductions could be as large as the difference between summer and winter. After such a 'nuclear winter', average temperatures would probably not return to normal for more than a year. The climate might be disturbed for years.

8 Some of the smoke and dust would settle to the ground soon after the main nuclear attacks, and some in the following weeks and months. There would be serious and widespread radioactive fallout and pollution in most of the heavily populated parts of the Northern Hemisphere. When the dust and smoke clear, the Earth's surface would probably be exposed to additional damaging ultraviolet radiation.

Even without a nuclear winter, the effects of nuclear war would be catastrophic. Chapter two summarizes the results of studies on the direct effects of nuclear war, and then discusses how nuclear war could break out and how it might be fought. To be specific, a definite 'scenario' is chosen and used as a basis for an account of the amount of dust and the size of the fires that the explosions would generate. Chapter three then shows what this does to the atmosphere around the cities and other targets.

The wind would spread the black cloud of smoke and

dust from the areas of conflict, and affect the atmosphere on a global scale. Chapter four describes what is expected to happen and the way that the cloud could make it dark and cold at the Earth's surface. After discussing how the climate could be affected in different parts of the world, the chapter continues with an account of some of the principal scientific investigations that have led to these predictions. It concludes with a description of the likely climatic effects of the war scenario of chapter two.

Unless nuclear war occurs, the nuclear winter predictions will remain a theory. In spite of two or three years intensive work by many very able scientists, the uncertainties in the predictions remain very real. These uncertainties are discussed in chapter 5. To indicate the range of predictions that are allowed by present evidence, a relatively mild and a relatively severe scenario of the climatic effects of a major nuclear war are described. There is also an assessment of how large-scale a nuclear war must be before there is a significant chance of triggering a nuclear winter.

If it came, the nuclear winter would have a devastating effect on living things. If the worst predictions were fulfilled, nuclear war and nuclear winter could wipe out most plants and animals in the Northern Hemisphere, severely damage life in the Southern Hemisphere, and threaten the survival of the human species. But even the mildest predictions suggest that harvests would be lost throughout the north temperate zone. Combined with world-wide economic chaos, this would bring starvation to millions of survivors.

Between these extremes, present knowledge suggests biological effects could include:

1 Very little plant growth for several months in the Northern Hemisphere, because of low light and temperatures.

2 Harvest failure throughout the Northern Hemisphere and poor harvests in the Southern Hemisphere in

the first year. Probable reduction in harvests for a further two or three years or longer.

3 The death of countless wild plants and animals and extinction of many species. Severe damage to forests, especially tropical forests. Some may never recover.

4 The collapse of advanced agriculture. Nearly everywhere, at least in the Northern hemisphere, only primitive subsistence farming would be possible for many years.

5 The collapse of medical and public-health services. Epidemic diseases would spread unchecked because there would be few doctors and no modern drugs.

6 The death from famine and epidemics within a few years, of more people than died in the nuclear war itself. Human suffering would be world-wide and on a scale almost beyond comprehension.

These are not fanciful speculations. Many scientists and doctors have reached independently much the same conclusions. We discuss in chapter 6 the long-term effects of nuclear war on plants and animals and chapter 7 is about the effects on human beings.

The nuclear winter findings mean that the nuclear powers have inadvertently built an unreliable Doomsday machine. In chapter 8 we consider the implications of this for national and international policies, give an account of the risks and uncertainties, and discuss what might be done to lessen the dangers.

Albert Einstein greatly regretted his contribution to the development of the atomic bomb during World War Two. The year after atomic bombs had been dropped on Hiroshima and Nagasaki he warned:

A new type of thinking is essential if mankind is to survive . . .

With the development of thermonuclear weapons and the newly realized danger of a nuclear winter, this new type of thinking has become an urgent necessity. We have to rethink the meaning of peace and of war, of defence and security and of conflict and co-operation between nations. If we do not, we may well be the last generation to have the choice.

Because the nuclear winter threatens everyone's future, we are all involved — there is no escape into bunkers in the ground or into the bunkers of the mind. Now that the risk to all of humanity is clear, there are new opportunities to find the common ground needed to remove the threat to our existence. This is the theme of our final chapter.

2 Fires and the Scale of Nuclear War

Introduction

The effects of a nuclear war on the Earth's climate would be mainly caused by smoke from fires and dust created by the explosions. The more smoke and dust were produced, and the higher they went, the more severe the climatic changes would become. So the risk of nuclear winter depends critically on the answers to questions such as: If nuclear war ever occurs, how large-scale is it likely to be? Against which targets would the various warheads be used? What areas would be set on fire? How much dust would the explosions generate?

This chapter looks into these issues. It will become clear just how vast the areas set on fire and the amount of dust created would probably be. But we begin with a brief review of the immediate consequences of nuclear war. This serves as an important reminder that nuclear war would be a catastrophe even without a nuclear winter.

The Effects of Nuclear War

If a thermonuclear weapon exploded over an inhabited area, the heat from the nuclear fireball would ignite fires and burn people miles away. The blast from the explosion would devastate areas of as much as hundreds of square miles. Radioactive fallout could kill or injure people over a hundred miles downwind. A single nuclear explosion over central London could cause 1,600,000 casualties by its blast effects alone.[1]

The destructive potential of nuclear weapons is so immense that their explosive energy, or yield, is usually measured in terms of thousands of tons (kilotons) or millions of tons (megatons) of the high explosive TNT. The bomb detonated over Hiroshima had a yield of 12.5 kilotons, equivalent to 12,500 tons of TNT. Warheads in the nuclear arsenals of today range in yield from less than one hundred tons of TNT to over 20 megatons. By comparison, all of the weapons used by all sides in World War Two had a total explosive power of less than five megatons.

Not surprisingly, in view of the devastating effects of a single nuclear explosion, the direct effects of a nuclear war are predicted to be catastrophic. The blast, heat and short-term radiation from a 220 megaton nuclear attack on the UK would probably kill at least 70 per cent of the population and seriously injure over 9 per cent.[2] If about one-third of the world's nuclear arsenal were used in a global nuclear war, the direct effects alone would kill between a few hundred million and one billion people (up to a quarter of the entire human race) and injure many millions of others.[3]

This takes no account of the consequences of widespread fires, lack of food, fuel and medical care, and all of the other terrible hazards of the aftermath. In Europe, the USSR and the USA, where most of the targets are located, industrial and agricultural production would collapse and society would probably disintegrate. The economies of developing countries are fragile at the best of times. They are often dependent on trade with (and aid from) the developed world, and would probably be unable to withstand the shock of an East–West nuclear war. Hundreds of millions more people in these regions could die of starvation and disease.[4]

Even without the nuclear winter, some one-and-a-half billion people — about one-third of the world's population — could die as a result of a large-scale nuclear war. The nuclear winter threatens the other two-thirds.

The World's Nuclear Arsenals

In 1946, after Hiroshima and Nagasaki, the USA alone possessed atomic bombs and even these few weapons were in various stages of construction. Today there are about 50,000 nuclear warheads in the world, nearly all in the arsenals of the USA, USSR, UK, France and China. These warheads come in a variety of different designs and are carried on missiles, aircraft, submarines, ships, and helicopters, or can be fired from artillery.

Nuclear weapons are usually categorized as 'strategic', 'theatre', or 'tactical' ('battlefield'), according to their range and purpose. Strategic weapons are long-range. They are often assumed to be targeted on the US or USSR, though some of them would probably be used against critical targets elsewhere. Theatre weapons are of medium range, with Europe or some other theatre of war as a primary target. Tactical weapons would be used in local battles. These distinctions are crude and can be misleading. For the nuclear winter, what matters most is the numbers and explosive powers of the warheads and their likely type of target.

Note: Table 2.1 shows the approximate nuclear weapon stockpiles maintained at present. It is based on information from a wide range of sources (especially those listed in note 25, chapter 2). The data are more reliable for US and USSR strategic weapons than for other categories.
Key: ICBM — intercontinental ballistic missiles; SLBM — submarine-launched ballistic missiles; ASM — air to surface missiles; MRBM — medium range ballistic missiles; SLCM — sea-launched cruise missiles; all others — naval and battlefield weapons, bombs; ~ — particularly approximate; > — greater than.

Table 2.1 The nuclear weapon stockpiles

Weapon type	Total number of deliverable warheads (approx)	Total yield in megatons (approx)
STRATEGIC WEAPONS		
USA:		
ICBM	2,137	1,302
SLBM	5,344	367
ASM	~2,160	~400
Bombs	~1,080	~960
USA sub-total (approx)	10,700	3,000
USSR:		
ICBM	5,600	4,000
SLBM	2,130	930
ASM	~30	~12
Bombs	~320	~1,610
USSR sub-total (approx)	8,100	6,500
THEATRE/TACTICAL WEAPONS		
USA:		
MRBM/SLCM	414	66
All others Europe	~5,600	>2,200
Elsewhere	~9,300	
USSR:		
Missiles	3,340	760
All others	~11,000	>2,000
Subtotal (approx)	29,700	>5,000
China:		
Missiles	~130	~170
Bombs	~220	~120
France:		
Missiles	142	102
Bombs	~205	4
UK:	~470	~130
Subtotal (approx)	1,170	530
Overall total	~49,600	>15,000

The existing nuclear arsenals are shown in table 2.1. The USA can now 'deliver' about 10,700 strategic nuclear warheads with a total yield of 3,000 megatons to the USSR, while the USSR can deliver about 8,100 warheads, with a yield of 6,500 megatons to the USA. Together with the 5,500 or more megatons carried on some 32,000 theatre and tactical weapons and on French, Chinese and British warheads, this makes over 15,000 megatons in all. This is enough to destroy more than eight times over every town in the world with over 100,000 inhabitants.

Targeting Plans

Past wars have lasted for weeks or years and so leaders have been able to change their strategies as they went along. In a nuclear war, however, most of the major attacks could be over in hours. Command centres could be destroyed within minutes, leaving forces uncoordinated. So, in the midst of the conflict there would be no time to adjust today's enormous and complex nuclear forces to operate in new ways. Commanders would have to follow plans prepared before the war started. This makes the targets of nuclear attacks in some ways more predictable than targets have traditionally been in war.

If nuclear war ever starts, both superpowers intend to try to use their nuclear forces to achieve military and political objectives, not just mutual suicide. This involves targeting a whole range of military, economic, administrative and leadership centres. Targets depend on objectives. The US Defense Intelligence Agency has identified no less than 500,000 sites of some military importance in the USSR. Of these, some 40,000 have been included in the US Department of Defense's SIOP-6; the latest Single Integrated Operational Plan of how US nuclear forces could be used.[5] Presumably, the USSR has identified similar targets in NATO countries.[6] Since the number of potential targets is even greater than the numbers of warheads available to destroy them, priorities must be assigned. These are summarised in box 2.1.

Some people have argued that a nuclear war could be controlled and limited, so that only a small proportion of the nuclear arsenals would be used. The US SIOP-6 plan, at least, includes 'limited nuclear options'. However, the weight of the evidence indicates that, once started, a nuclear war between East and West is very likely to escalate to large-scale attacks.[7] In fact, even leading supporters of 'limited nuclear options', such as President Reagan and President Carter's Secretary of Defense, Harold Brown, have said that they would not expect a nuclear war to remain limited in practice.[8] In this book we are concerned with what would actually happen if nuclear war occurred, not with what one needs to pretend could happen in order to make 'nuclear deterrence' seem credible. So from now on we will concentrate on large-scale nuclear war, although the effects of limited nuclear war will be referred to occasionally.

Once large-scale nuclear war begins, or appears inevitable, there would be intense pressure to launch most of the nuclear forces quickly. Otherwise they could be destroyed or isolated by enemy attacks. In fact both the USA and the USSR seem prepared to launch early massive attacks in order to disrupt and destroy many of the enemy forces before they can be used.[9] The superpowers might hope that such early nuclear strikes could at least limit the levels of devastation they would suffer.

The opponent's nuclear forces and command and control system would be the top priority targets (see box 2.1). Conventional military installations and forces would be destroyed to prevent them from being used during or after the initial nuclear exchanges. In any case they are often closely integrated with the nuclear forces. 'War-supporting' industries and resources such as defence

Box 2.1

Targeting Categories

In March, 1980, the US Department of Defense gave the following examples of targets within their four targeting categories.[10]

Soviet Nuclear Forces (more than 2,000 targets)

Intercontinental and intermediate range ballistic missile forces, together with their launch facilities and launch command centres; nuclear weapon storage sites; Airfields supporting nuclear-capable aircraft; nuclear missile-firing submarine bases.

Military and Political Leadership (about 3,000 targets)

Command posts; key communications facilities; (plus early warning, radar, and other intelligence gathering bases).

Conventional military forces (about 15,000 targets)

Caserns; supply depots; marshalling points, conventional airfields, ammunition storage facilities; tank and vehicle storage yards; (plus naval bases, air defence installations, and so on).

Economic and industrial targets (about 15,000 targets)

a War-supporting industry: ammunition factories; tank and armoured personnel carrier factories; petroleum refineries; railway yards and repair facilities; (plus ports, civil airfields, aircraft factories, defence electronics industry).

b Industry that contributes to economic recovery: coal, basic steel, basic aluminium, cement, electrical power.

The US Department of Defense only intended this list to be illustrative — there could be many other examples within each category. The examples in brackets were added by us to provide a fuller set of examples.

Soviet categorization and priorities would be similar. An indication of Soviet targeting plans is given by the following quotation from Soviet military writings (see also note 6, chapter 2).

[The initial Soviet missile strike would be a massive strike on the] aggressor's means of nuclear attack and simultaneous mass destruction of vital installations comprising the enemy's military, political, and economic might.[11]

industries, ports, petroleum refineries, power stations, and railway junctions, would be the next priority in order to undermine the enemy's war effort.

Finally, both the US and the USSR appear to plan to attack targets to prevent the other from recovering first in the years after the war. Thus Donald Rumsfeld explained when he was US Secretary of State; 'if the Soviet Union could emerge from (general war) with superior military power and could recuperate from the effects more rapidly than the United States, the US capability for assured retaliation would be considered inadequate.[12] So in order to hinder recovery, targets such as heavy industries, energy resources, fertilizer factories and civil administrative centres, and such like, are likely to come next on the list of targets. For similar reasons, 'preventive' attacks might also be launched against countries that were not yet involved in the conflict, in order to prevent them from dominating the world after the holocaust.

Ordinary people are low-priority targets. Military planners have clearly decided that any advantages from low public morale would be more than adequately achieved by all of the attacks listed above.

With their comparatively small nuclear arsenals, France, the UK and China have little hope of limiting damage by early attacks on the enemy's military forces unless they act in alliance with one of the superpowers. Thus, in contrast to the USA and USSR, urban centres and economic facilities are likely to be the primary targets for these lesser nuclear powers.

The Possibility of Nuclear War

In spite of the immense devastation that a nuclear war would cause, it is certainly possible for one to occur in our lifetimes. Many believe that this is even probable if present trends continue.

Local wars and political confrontations often escalate far beyond anyone's initial intentions. One danger is that the superpowers will get sucked into a war which then develops into a nuclear war that no one wanted. Furthermore, as the relative advantage of striking first rather than second in a nuclear war increases, international crises are becoming more unstable.

Technical or human failures are possible. As the intelligence and control systems become more automated and the time available to double check a warning of nuclear attack shortens, the chance of war occurring by accident or misperception is growing, particularly during a period of tension when both sides would be on alert. The American Pershing IIs and the (less accurate) Soviet missiles in submarines in the Western Atlantic can destroy prime military targets and command centres in ten minutes or less.

If present trends continue, more and more countries can be expected to acquire nuclear weapons. The arguments used by the UK, France and China to justify their own nuclear arsenals can be used by any other country in the world. Every extra country with nuclear weapons increases the chance of nuclear war.

The Cuban missile crisis brought the world close to

nuclear war in 1962. A similar event today could easily prove catastrophic.

A Nuclear War Scenario

Although some scenarios are more plausible than others, no one can predict exactly how a nuclear war would happen and how it would be fought. Here is one way in which a nuclear war could develop.

Instabilities in the Middle East provoke the USA to intervene in order to support an ally and protect the oil wells which it regards as vital to the Western economy. The USSR regards the US intervention as illegitimate and, since the region is close to its borders, potentially hostile. It moves in to support its own allies in the region. As the superpowers are drawn into direct conflict the crisis escalates and NATO and Warsaw Pact forces are put on red alert and forces in Europe are mobilized.

Border incidents are provoked and reprisals are taken along the East–West German frontier as each superpower and its alliance seeks to frighten the other into backing down. As a precaution against pre-emptive attack, orders are given to disperse battlefield nuclear warheads from their vulnerable storage sites. Ground-launched Cruise and Pershing II missiles are dispersed for the same reason. Other tactical nuclear weapons are flown to Europe from the USA and the USSR.

Each side's intelligence services detect the other's preparations for nuclear war and suspect the worst. Pre-emptive attacks with conventional weapons are launched against these preparations but they rapidly escalate. Within a few days, the first tactical nuclear weapons are used by local military commanders in Germany to defend important military bases.

Soon afterwards short and medium-range nuclear forces are used without restraint in Europe and the

Middle East. The USSR uses large numbers of theatre and tactical nuclear forces on military and economic targets throughout western Europe. A few Soviet strategic missiles are used against some of the prime military targets in the UK and western Europe. The US and its NATO allies do likewise on eastern Europe. A partially successful attempt is made to destroy British and French missile submarines in port or at sea before they are able to launch their missiles.

The US and the USSR initially try to avoid attacking each other's territory, in the desperate hope of ending the war before their own countries are destroyed. Cruise and Pershing II missiles are launched to avoid the inevitable heavy attacks aimed at destroying them. But they are used against targets in eastern Europe rather than the USSR. As Soviet strategic forces are by now placed on 'launch on warning' alert, the launch of these US missiles almost triggers an automatic response. However, in a last bid for national survival, the Soviet leadership intervenes to prevent any immediate strategic attacks.

For a short period, the pace of the escalation slows. Bombers are dispersed and, where possible, submarines are put to sea. However, the uncoordinated action of military commanders soon carries the war into the western districts of the USSR. Also, the surviving British and French commanders launch their remaining nuclear forces towards the cities and industrial areas of western USSR.

Believing that global war is now inevitable, both superpowers almost simultaneously launch all-out counterforce attacks on enemy military bases, followed by massive attacks on economic targets and other resources important to recovery after the war. Attacks are launched on China to destroy its nuclear forces and prevent it from dominating the world after the war.

Nuclear strikes outside of NATO and Warsaw Pact countries or China are extensive, particularly against the overseas military bases of the superpowers and their allies. The USA has many such bases in Japan, Australia, South Korea, Guam, Subic Bay in the Phillipines, Diego Garcia in the Indian Ocean and on a number of Pacific islands. There are Soviet military factilities in Cuba, Cam Ranh Bay in Vietnam, Dahlak Island in Ethiopia, Aden in South Yemen and elsewhere.[13]

Some communications links, sources of fuel and economic centres in the non-belligerent countries are also attacked to prevent enemy forces from gaining access to them. For example, in the Middle East, where the war is assumed to start in our scenario, many of the oil wells are destroyed.

Israel is thought to have a few Hiroshima-style nuclear warheads, and South Africa could also have built a few.[14] Some of these weapons may be used in an attempt to settle regional conflicts during a global war. However, the number of weapons is so small in comparison with the nuclear stockpiles of the superpowers that they are neglected in this scenario.

Altogether just less than 18,000 warheads are used with a combined yield of about 6,000 megatons — approximately 40 per cent of the total world arsenal (see table 2.2 and appendix 2.1). Most of the explosions are assumed to be in the northern midlatitudes, stretching from the Arctic Circle (North Norway) to the Tropic of Cancer (Miami in the USA), where the overwhelming majority of the targets — and about half the world's population (see figure 2.1) — are located. Only a few of the warheads are assumed to be used in the Southern Hemisphere.

Most of the warheads containing the remaining 9,000 megatons are assumed to have been destroyed by enemy attacks before they could be used or to have malfunctioned so that they did not detonate. Some warheads would explode at sea or at high altitudes where they would generate little dust and few fires and can therefore be neglected for our purposes (although smoke from damaged oil rigs at sea could be significant).[15] Finally, the

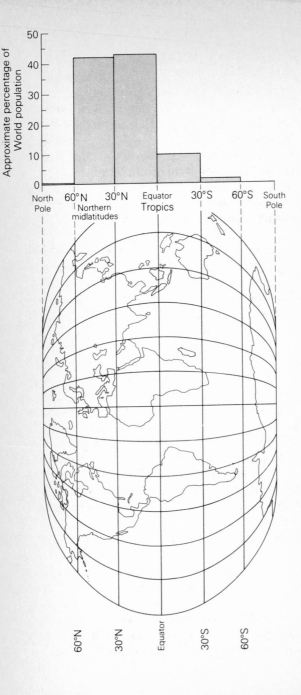

Figure 2.1. The distribution of the World's population

Note: The map shows how the Earth's population is concentrated in the Northern Hemisphere, where most of the targets are located and, as will become clear, where the effects of a nuclear winter would be most severe.

Table 2.2 Summary of nuclear war scenario

Nuclear forces	Warheads used	Yield used		Yield (in megatons) used against				
		Megatons	% of total (approx)	Missile fields	USA + Canada (nonsilo)	USSR (nonsilo)	Europe	Else-where
US strategic	6,409	1,400	46	692	—	620	49	39
USSR strategic	4,207	2,789	43	1,107	1,433	—	184	65
USA theatre/ tactical	3,439	755	<33	—	—	67	646	42
USSR theatre/ tactical	3,461	884	<30	—	—	—	668	216
UK	146	44	33	—	—	32	12	—
France	118	44	42	—	—	43	1	—
China	87	86	29	—	10	66	—	10
TOTAL	17,867	6,002	~40	1,799	1,443	828	1,560	372

Note: 3414 megatons are groundburst of which some 2,760 megatons is on warheads of yield greater than or equal to half a megaton.

USA USSR may hold back some nuclear warheads to restore 'nuclear deterrence' in the aftermath.

This is only one of many possible nuclear war scenarios. However, we will use it to estimate the scale of dust and fire effects resulting from a nuclear war. We begin by reviewing some of the effects of nuclear explosions and, particularly, the areas they could ignite and the amounts of dust that they could generate.

Nuclear Explosions

The energy from a nuclear explosion comes from the strong forces that hold the particles of the nucleus of an atom together and from the electrical forces between them. When the warhead is detonated, there is an immediate flash of light and neutron and gamma rays. X-rays from the explosion heat the surrounding air, creating a massive nuclear fireball which is as hot as the sun.[16]

Fire and blast

Between about one-quarter and one-third of the energy released by the bomb is radiated as heat away from the fireball. This heat is so intense that exposed wood, fabrics, plastics, and other inflammable materials would be set on fire up to several miles away.

The area of fire ignition depends on the height and yield of the explosion, the weather, and the materials in the target area. As shown in table 2.3, for an 'airburst', where the fireball does not touch the ground, the area varies between about 55 and 250 squares miles (140–625 square kilometers) on a reasonably clear day. The ignition area of a 'groundburst', where the fireball does touch the ground, is usually smaller; between 40 and 130 square miles (100–320 square kilometers).

Table 2.3 Fire ignition zones from nuclear explosions

Warhead yield (megatons)	Airburst			Groundburst		
	Ignition area sq. miles	Ignition area/megaton sq. miles	Ignition area/megaton sq. km	Ignition area sq. miles	Ignition area/megaton sq. miles	Ignition area/megaton sq. km
10	550	55	140	370	37	95
1	120	120	315	80	80	205
0.1	20	190	495	11	110	285
0.01	2.45	245	625	1.3	130	330

Note: Table 2.3 shows the 'ignition zones' (where the thermal flux is more than 12 calories/sq. cm.) caused by the detonation of a range of groundburst and airburst warheads. Note that scattered fires could be ignited beyond the defined ignition zone. The figures apply in conditions of 12-mile visibility with no cloud or snow cover. Based on data from S. Glasstone and P. Dolan, *The effects of nuclear weapons*, (note 16, chapter 2). For further discussion of ignition zones, see appendix 2.2.

Roughly half of the energy of the bomb goes to form a blast wave which can devastate areas several miles from the detonation point. Mild blast damage could extend to tens of miles away. The winds associated with the blast would extinguish fires in some places. In other locations they might fan the flames and spread the fire by carrying burning materials along with them.[17]

Urban areas close to the detonation point would be totally destroyed. Here the materials that can burn would be mixed with rubble and the fires would tend to burn relatively slowly, producing thick smoke.[18] However, the area of total devastation would typically make up only about one-tenth of the ignition zone. In the remainder of the zone the lesser blast damage would 'open up' buildings and spread debris. This would help the fire to spread and burn intensely. Smashed doors and windows and damaged roofs beyond the ignition zone would help the conflagration spread outwards to neighbouring areas. Furthermore, blast-damaged gas, fuel, electrical, industrial and other plants would start secondary fires both within and beyond the ignition zone. In other words, on balance, blast would encourage the development of mass fires.[19]

The effects of a nuclear explosion over a city are illustrated in box 2.2, which shows some of the consequences of a one megaton airburst over Whitehall in London.

In woodland, grasslands, or agricultural areas the extent of the fires would depend very much upon the weather and the season. At any one time in summer, about half of all the burnable materials are medium to highly inflammable. So fires could be readily ignited by the heat from nuclear fireballs, though with peacetime firefighting services (which are not likely to operate after a nuclear war) they would normally not be expected to spread to cover more than double the area of the initial ignition zone. However, after a drought and if humidity is low, such fires could spread uncontrollably over large

Box 2.2

A Single Bomb over London

Suppose a one megaton bomb explodes about 10,000 feet above Whitehall, London, on a clear day. Anyone looking towards it from as far away as Luton (32 miles) is temporarily blinded by the initial brilliant flash of light. Windows are smashed over 18 miles away.

Key

Blast: Zone A Almost total destruction.
                Blast casualties: 98% dead, 2% serious injuries

        Zone B Houses destroyed, reinforced concrete
                shells remain, blast winds over 160 mph.
                Blast casualties: 50% dead, 40% serious injuries

        Zone C Houses severely damaged, roofs destroyed.
                Blast casualties: 5% dead, 45% serious injuries

        Zone D Windows and doors smashed, roofs damaged.
                Casualties from flying glass and debris: 25% injured

        Zone E Windows smashed, no blast casualties.

Fire: Fire ignition zone (thermal flux >12 calories/cm^2)
                High density of fires started by the heat from
                the nuclear fireball.

                Limit of area where fires ignited by heat of fireball
                and where blast likely to start secondary fires.

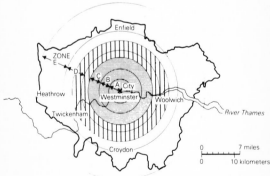

Blast and fire effects of a one megaton airburst over London.

Note: This is only illustrative: in a realistic attack scenario, London would be affected by several nuclear explosions.

(continued)

People and materials close to the explosion are vaporized. Direct heat from the fireball sets combustible materials alight over an area of more than 120 square miles (310 sq km). Secondary fires are started over an even larger area as a result of the blast. Burning plastics and chemicals produce large amounts of poisonous fumes.

As far as 8 miles away unprotected people suffer second-degree burns (blistered skin) or worse. Even assuming that only one person in twenty is exposed, up to one hundred thousand people are fatally or seriously burned. Over half a million people are at risk from fires and fumes. At present there are only 106 beds for severely burned patients in the whole of the UK.[20]

Blast destroys almost everything for about 2.5 miles. Out at 4.5 miles people are killed by falling masonry or lifted by winds of more than 160 mph and hurled into obstacles. Some 12 miles away people are slashed by glass from windows, roof tiles and other debris flying through the air at about 70 mph.

If the bomb had been a groundburst, the area of blast and heat effects would be expected to be somewhat smaller. However, local fallout would result in intense radioactivity many miles downwind. Assuming a steady 15 mph wind, people without fallout shelters could receive lethal doses of radiation as far away as Portsmouth and beyond Oxford (60 miles). People about 90 miles away (such as in Coventry or Kings Lynn) could suffer from acute radiation sickness.

---

areas. In winter, on the other hand, only a small proportion of the fuels will burn and so it would be hard for the fires to sustain themselves in temperate zones, let alone spread.[21]

The blast from the nuclear explosions would flatten forests and spread torn-off branches over the ground well beyond the ignition zone. This would expose areas of dry wood that would otherwise be protected by bark and by living wood. It would also uproot trees, exposing roots and mixing the crowns of the trees with burning material on the ground. This would make any wildfires much more likely to spread than normal. It would also tend to increase the intensity of the fires, and this has important implications (as will become clear in chapter three).

Overlap of the ignition zones from neighbouring explosions would reduce the overall fire area, although this may be partially counterbalanced by the tendency for nearby conflagrations to generate winds that spread the fires into the gaps between them.[22] The dust and smoke caused by one explosion is likely to block some of the heat from a second explosion nearby. On the other hand, areas affected by more than one explosion would be more likely to ignite. The first pulse of heat would desiccate materials so that they would be more susceptible to the second pulse. The blast of the first bomb would also tend to expose inflammable materials to the heat from the second.

Fire ignition is discussed in more detail in appendix 2.2, and the likely characteristics of 'nuclear' fires and the smoke they would generate is dealt with in chapter three.

Dust and Radioactive Fallout

Meanwhile, as the blast wave spreads, the hot fireball from the nuclear explosion would rise high into the air to form the characteristic mushroom cloud, sweeping large amounts of material and radioactive debris up with it.

For an airburst nuclear weapons tests indicate that about 10,000 tonnes of dust per megaton, together with the material from the bomb and its casing, would be swept up into the atmosphere by the winds created by the rising fireball.[23] A groundburst would also gouge out an enormous crater — large enough to house ten Wembley stadiums in the case of a one megaton explosion (see

Figure 2.2. Photograph of the formation of the dust cloud from a groundburst nuclear explosion

Note: From S. Glasstone and P. Dolan, *The effects of nuclear weapons*, (note 16, chapter 2).

figure 2.2). For every megaton exploded, between 200,000 and 500,000 tonnes of dust would be carried into the atmosphere.[24]

The height to which the dust is carried by the fireball mainly depends on the yield of the warhead. For yields greater than a few hundred kilotons, most of the dust would be carried into the upper part of the atmosphere, where it would remain for months or years. Lower-yield weapons would send most of the dust into the lower part of the atmosphere, where it would normally return to the ground within a few weeks.

The fine particles that remain in the atmosphere for weeks to years are known as intermediate-timescale and long-term radioactive fallout when they return to the ground. In the case of a groundburst, however, much of the dust would fall to the Earth within a day or so as highly radioactive local fallout.

Fire Ignition and the Nuclear War Scenario

The risk of nuclear winter comes mainly from smoke from fires started by the nuclear attacks. The quantities of smoke produced depend on four factors: the area burnt, the amount of fuel available in this area, the fraction of this fuel that is actually consumed by fire, and the proportion of the burnt material that becomes smoke.

Here we consider the first factor: ignition zones — the area ignited by the heat from the nuclear fireballs. The other parts of this problem are addressed in chapter three. Since urban centres and, to a lesser extent, forests contain a particularly high density of inflammable material, these receive special attention. Fires on grass and agricultural land and at oil or gas wells and fuel stores are also briefly considered. A more detailed description of the assumptions and calculations is provided in appendix 2.3.

Applying the ignition zone areas given in table 2.3 and appendix 2.2 to each of the warheads used in the nuclear attack scenario, it is easy to calculate the maximum area of the ignition zone (if we assume no fire spread). It is phenomenal: almost the combined area of the EEC countries (excluding Spain and Portugal), that is about 625,000 square miles (1,600,000 square kilometers). However, in practice many of the ignition zones would overlap. So fires would actually be ignited over a somewhat smaller area than this.

The target areas where overlap and double targeting

would be greatest are the missile fields where the intercontinental ballistic missiles are kept ready for launch. These will therefore be considered separately.

The next most heavily attacked region would probably be Europe. More than 10,000 nuclear warheads carrying over 3,000 megatons are currently likely to be allocated to this densely targeted region.[25] Even the 1,560 megatons that we take to be used on Europe would devastate much of this continent.

Central Europe would be the most damaged area because thousands of short-range battlefield weapons would be used there in addition to medium and intermediate-range nuclear forces. Countries such as the UK, Italy, France, Hungary and Poland would also be heavily attacked. Most of the other countries in Europe could expect at least severe damage and wide-spread fires.

Figure 2.3 shows a map of the ignition zones resulting from a 220 megaton attack on the UK. The total area of these zones would be about 19,500 square miles (49,000 square kilometers) — almost two-and-a-half times the area of Wales. They include almost two-thirds of the present population, most of the major urban areas, large tracts of agricultural and wooded land, most large coal, oil and nuclear power stations, and nearly all of the main oil and gas refineries and terminals.[26] In the UK, as in the rest of densely populated Europe, few military targets are far away from towns or cities.

The attack on the UK involved extensive double targeting and, as can be seen from the figure, a large amount of overlap of the ignition zones. Using this example as a guide, it is assumed that overlap reduces the ignition area by an average of 20 per cent throughout Europe. In the USA, USSR and elsewhere, the targets would be more dispersed (apart from missile silos which are considered separately), and overlap can be taken to reduce the area by ten per cent. Thus we assume that the average ignition zone is reduced from about 115 square

Figure 2.3. The ignition zones caused by a nuclear attack on the
UK

Note: The map shows the areas in which fires could be ignited by a 220 megaton
nuclear attack on the UK. The attack is largely on military targets and on a
limited number of defence and basic industries. It is described, together with its
consequences, in detail in the book *Doomsday* (note 2, chapter 2). It is assumed
that cruise missiles have *not* been dispersed. If they had been, the ignition zones
could cover nearly all of the south and east of England.

miles (290 square kilometers) per megaton to about 90 and 103 square miles (230 and 260 square kilometers) per megaton for Europe and elsewhere respectively. These figures are roughly in line with the more conservative of the estimates made by the NRC, TTAPS and other studies.[27]

Taking all targets into account, the ignition zones would be likely to cover more than 500,000 square miles of land, including enormous areas of forest and towns — an area of about ten times the size of England. It is scarcely surprising that suddenly starting fires over such a vast area could have dire effects on the Earth's climate. We now show how this estimate of the total ignition zone has been arrived at.

Urban Ignition Zones

In any major nuclear war, large numbers of warheads are bound to detonate over or near to urban centres. Many command, control, or communications centres are associated with cities. Washington, Omaha, Moscow, Leningrad, London and Frankfurt are a few prime examples. Naval bases, airfields and other military targets are often close to towns and cities, as are defence and other key industries. For example, all 200 of the largest Soviet cities and 80 per cent of the 886 Soviet cities with populations above 25,000 are included in US targeting plans, purely because they are associated with military or industrial targets.[28]

There are about 2260 urban centres (cities plus their surrounding urban conglomerations and suburbs) in the world with population of more than 100,000 people. Together they contain roughly 1,500 million people, with an average population density of some 2,500 people per square mile. About 85 per cent of these urban areas are in the Northern Hemisphere and there are over 1,100 large cities within NATO or Warsaw Pact countries.[29] That so many people and economic resources are concentrated in relatively few places, and these mainly in the Northern

Hemisphere, illustrates how vulnerable human civilization is to nuclear war. An initial estimate of the urban areas within ignition zones can be obtained by examining these cities alone.

A moderate estimate is that about one-fifth of the total yield used in the scenario is detonated over cities or their surrounding conurbations. For our calculations we assume that only about 30 per cent of the large urban centres in the USA and USSR, and 40 per cent in Europe, would be within ignition zones. Less than 90 cities in Canada, Japan, China and elsewhere in the world are also taken to be affected. On these assumptions, an urban area of about 190 times the size of Greater London (i.e. about 117,000 square miles — 300,000 square kilometers) would be within the ignition zone.

The scale of many of these fires would be quite unprecedented. Even if only two-thirds or less of each of the affected cities were actually within the ignition zones, many of the largest city fires would be ignited almost simultaneously over more than 400 square miles. It is very likely that in many of these cities fire would spread, and that secondary fires would lead to even larger areas of conflagrations. In comparison the fires in Hiroshima after the nuclear explosion covered 'only' 5 square miles and the fire area in Dresden spread over about 11 square miles.[30] Figure 2.4 illustrates possible ignition zones over Los Angeles.

In city centres the density of people, buildings and combustible materials is particularly high, and fires would burn very intensely. Typically these areas cover about one tenth of an urban centre, and so at least 12,000 square miles (30,000 square kilometers) of the city cores would be expected to burn.

In addition, many people and industries are located in smaller towns and villages. A crude estimate (see appendix 2.3) is that at least 38 million of these people would be in an ignition zone. This is equivalent to an urban sprawl of just less than the size of Switzerland (about 15,000 square miles).

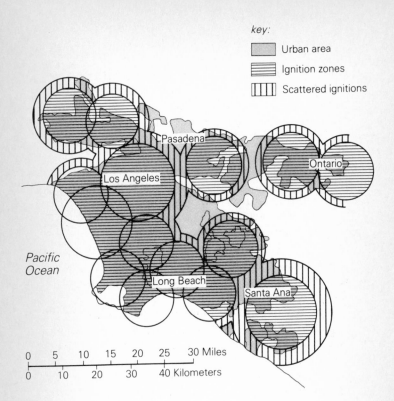

Figure 2.4. Ignition zones over Los Angeles

Note: The map illustrates the potential scale of urban fires by showing the ignition zones from an illustrative attack on the Los Angeles area. The attacks include one explosion over the city centre, but are mainly against military targets and airfields. The total yield used is **9** megatons.

Fire Ignition in Woodland and Grassland

As mentioned above, the intensity of the likely attacks on missile fields means that they must be considered separately.

Missile Fields

Altogether there are 31 intercontinental ballistic missile fields in the USA and USSR covering a total area of over 100,000 square miles (260,000 square kilometers). The double targeting and overlap of the ignition zones from attacks on missile silos is so great in our scenario that the area over which fires would be started would be simply the total area of the missile fields and their immediate surroundings.

In the USA, only one missile field and the Vandenburg test centre in California are located in forested regions, and only a proportion of even these bases is covered by trees. Only one-fortieth of the area of the US missile fields is assumed to be wooded, whereas four-fifths is assumed to be grass or agricultural land. The remainder is taken to be scrub. In contrast, in the USSR about half of the missile fields are in forested areas. Several of the remainder are in agricultural regions. We assume, conservatively, that only about one-third of the Soviet missile fields are forested.

In total, about 21,000 square miles (53,000 square kilometers) of forest and 62,000 square miles (158,000 square kilometers) of grass or agricultural land could be ignited by attacks on missile fields. The remainder would be scrubland or desert. Although there are small settlements which would probably be set alight, the urban area involved is so small, relatively speaking, that it can be ignored.

Elsewhere

Many warheads would be used outside of the large urban areas and missile fields against targets such as naval bases, air bases, radar and radio stations, troop concentrations, depots, transport links and industrial centres. Because of human and technical errors, many warheads could detonate far from any intended target. Some of the most densely targeted areas in Europe, notably central Europe, are also amongst the most heavily forested. In North America and the USSR a large number of military targets are in forested regions. The 24 Pinetree Line early-warning radars in southern Canada are an example of this.

Perhaps surprisingly, about 40 per cent of the total land surface of the Earth is (still) forested, as is a similar proportion of the land in the NATO and Warsaw Pact countries.[31] So assuming that forested areas make up a similar proportion of the ignition zone outside missile fields and cities, about 110,000 square miles (280,000 square kilometers) of woodland could be set on fire. This is about equal to the combined area of West Germany and the Netherlands. Roughly the same area of grass and agricultural land is also likely to be ignited.

Fuel Stores

Oil and gas wells are likely to be priority targets, as are major refineries and fuel stores. About 1.5 billion tons of fossil fuel is currently stored around the world, and there are about 600,000 oil and gas wells. Most of the world's oil and gas production comes from the NATO and Warsaw Pact regions and form the Middle East — all areas likely to be heavily attacked. If many of these fuel stores were set on fire, vast quantities of thick smoke would be produced.[32] However, fires at the wells would burn relatively slowly, lasting weeks or months. This reduces their importance as far as climatic changes are concerned, as is explained in the following chapters.

Dust and the Nuclear War Scenario

Although smoke is likely to have the greatest effect on the climate, the dust sent high into the atmosphere by the explosion would also be important. In the scenario, 57 per cent of the total yield was groundburst, implying that between 0.7 and 1.7 billion tonnes of dust would be sent into the atmosphere (see page 28), the most likely quantity being about one billion tonnes.[33] Over three-quarters of this would be generated by warheads with a yield of more than 500 kilotons, so most of the dust would be carried into the upper part of the atmosphere.

Conclusions

Our 6,000 megaton nuclear war scenario would ignite fires over areas bigger than many countries. Making conservative assumptions, the combined area of cities and their surrounding conurbations within the ignition zone would be roughly the size of Italy. For smaller towns and villages, the corresponding area could just about cover Switzerland. Fires could be started in forests over an area of more than five times the combined size of the Benelux countries, and the total ignition zones over grass or agricultural land would cover the UK about two times over. Finally, enough dust would be carried high into the atmosphere to dam the English channel with a wall 500 yards high and 30 yards thick. The actual estimates are summarized in table 2.4.

These estimates are only approximate. The area of the urban ignition zone could be larger if the fires spread or if the warheads were targeted so that more than one-fifth of the total yield used in the scenario was effective in starting city fires. In any case, some fires would be likely to be started outside our defined ignition zone. It is also possible that the total area could be less, although the assumptions we make are rather conservative. Previous estimates of urban fires have ranged from 100,000 to 200,000 square miles (250,000–500,000 square kilometers).[34] To be as sure as possible that the area of urban fires is not being exaggerated, we take the further conser-

Table 2.4 Summary of estimated ignition zones and dust generation caused by the nuclear war scenario

| Type of ignition area | Approximate area of ignition zones ('000s sq km) | | | | |
	USA + USSR Missile fields	Other	Elsewhere	Europe	Total
Large Urban Centres	—	110	38	153	301
Towns and Villages	—	14	4	21	39
Urban sub-total					340
Woodland	53	208		74	335
Grassland	158	208		74	440
Other	49	104		37	190

Total dust generated: approximately one billion tonnes

vative step of assuming throughout the rest of the book that they cover just 100,000 square miles (250,000 square kilometers).

The area of urban fires is unlikely to be greatly affected by the weather or season. This is not true of wildfires in forests and grasslands. Our estimates apply for a summer war. Even then the uncertainties for wildfires are very great. Under some conditions fires could spread so much that the area of wildfires could be a great deal larger than our estimate. But variations in weather and moisture levels could well reduce ignition zones by more than half. Previous estimates have ranged between 40,000 and 400,000 square miles (100,000–1,000,000 square kilometers).[35] In winter the areas of forest ignited could be less than one-tenth of our estimate.

Our scenario is only one of many possible ones. It should be clear from table 2.2 and appendix 2.1 that a nuclear war could be much bigger. A 10,000 megaton war involving about 30,000 warheads would still only use about two-thirds of the available weaponry. On the other hand the war could be more limited, although it is hard to believe that a nuclear war between NATO and the Warsaw Pact would involve less than a few thousand megatons.

It is interesting — and sobering — to note that even relatively small-scale attacks would ignite enormous areas. The small proportion of the French and British forces used in our scenario could alone start city fires over some 12,000 square miles — more than 32 times the area of Moscow.[36] The attacks on Europe (excluding European USSR) in our scenario would ignite urban fires over an area about 108 times larger than Greater London (i.e. about 68,000 square miles).

The next two chapters show how the dust and smoke plumes resulting from our scenario would rise into the air and combine to form a black cloud which could make much of the Earth's surface cold and dark.

3 Fires, Smoke and the Atmosphere

Introduction

According to recent research, a nuclear winter would be caused mainly by smoke from fires rising high into the atmosphere, where it would be blown around the world by the wind, blocking out the light of the Sun. So in this chapter we describe the nature of fires in general, and in particular the enormous 'nuclear fires' ignited by nuclear weapons in the manner described in chapter 2. We continue with a description of the atmosphere and how the clouds of smoke and dust rise up into it.

Fires

A fire needs both oxygen and fuel to burn. The oxygen comes from the air, and the fuel can be anything 'combustible' — that is, anything that burns. A fire develops in several stages: ignition, establishment, spread and extinction.

It may start in many ways, including ignition by a match, a stroke of lightning, an incendiary bomb or a nuclear explosion. It becomes established by taking hold around the place or places where it was ignited, and it may then spread to other areas. For example, in a room with modern upholstered furniture, a fire might start in a chair, but go no further, or it might spread to carpets and other furniture, causing a 'flashover' of the whole room within five or ten minutes of ignition. As another example, a fire in a small grove of trees around a tree struck by lightning might burn, but go no further, or it might spread 'like wildfire' through a whole forest. A fire is finally extinguished by running out of fuel or oxygen, or by cooling of the fuel, or by some combination of these. In a nuclear war like that described in chapter 2 the most important fires would be in cities and sometimes in forests.

Natural forest fires are common during summer and autumn in many parts of the World, such as Canada and the USSR, and some of them have been very large. They can be started by lightning or by human carelessness, with very few ignition points, possibly only one. The establishment and spread of a fire depends very much on the success or failure of firefighters, and on weather conditions both before and during the fire. Huschke has made a survey of the percentage probability of establishment and significant spread of natural forest fires in the USA.[1] It varies from 60 per cent in the height of summer to near zero in midwinter.

Surprisingly, natural forest fires do not burn everything in their path. They tend to advance along irregular fronts, burning dry leaves or pine needles, the scrub or litter on the forest floor and some smaller branches, but the trunks of the trees usually remain largely unburnt. Typically it is observed that about 20 per cent of the combustible material burns, but there is wide variation from one fire to another. Roots and peat below ground sometimes burn for days or even months.

Fires in cities and towns are different from forest fires. Those of World War Two did not seem to be affected very much by the weather, probably because most of the material that could burn was indoors and dry. In the incendiary bomb attacks on Hamburg and Dresden and in the nuclear attack on Hiroshima there were firestorms, in which individual fires over a wide area joined together into one large fire. In these fires the proportion of combustible material that burnt was observed to be close to 100 per cent. Also sometimes there are forest firestorms.

The air drawn into any open fire is heated, expands and rises as a buoyant plume. The hot air is replaced by cooler air from around the fire, and in big fires this produces winds that blow inwards to the hottest part of the fire from well beyond its edge. In firestorms, the fire winds are so strong that they overcome any natural winds, and this tends to prevent the fires from spreading beyond the ignition zone, but virtually everything combustible is burned within it. When the fire wind is weaker, the fire is more likely to spread, but the proportion of material that burns is usually less.

Whether or not there is a firestorm, the height of the smoke plume depends primarily on the power of the fire, as is shown in the last section of this chapter.

Nuclear Fires

The fires of the nuclear war scenario described in chapter 2 covered a total area greater than the UK; what would they be like?

The fire area after the nuclear attack on Hiroshima is illustrated in figure 3.1. Experience with past fires, particularly those at Hiroshima and Nagasaki, can help us to understand what would happen in a nuclear war, but this information needs to be used with caution. Thermonuclear weapons have been tested in deserts, in the Arctic, on Pacific islands and underground, but fortunately never near cities or forests. We can be sure that many of the fires of a large-scale nuclear war would be different from anything that there has been before.

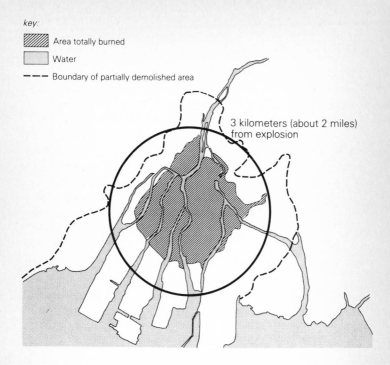

key:

⬛ Area totally burned

⬜ Water

– – – Boundary of partially demolished area

3 kilometers (about 2 miles) from explosion

Figure 3.1. Map of Hiroshima in 1945 with fire area of 13 kiloton nuclear explosion[2]

Note: The many waterways would normally impede the spread of fire.

The fires would differ in the density of ignition points. Near to the nuclear explosion nearly everything that burns would ignite, and from there the density of ignition points would decrease with distance from the explosion, out to the edge of the ignition zone, providing there was material to ignite. But even at 6 calories (about 25J) per square centimeter (half the heat intensity which we have assumed for the edge of the zone), fires could start in a significant fraction of dry forest litter or city rubbish.

Anything combustible that happened to be in the fireball of a groundburst would vaporize first, and then probably burn within the rising fireball, mixing smoke with the dust of the mushroom cloud.

The fires would differ in the size of their ignition zones. This was about 5 square miles (13 square kilometers) in Hiroshima, shown in Figure 3.1. Table 2.3 in chapter 2 shows that for most nuclear weapons it would be from about 40 to 250 square miles (100 to 600 square kilometers) for every megaton exploded, and a nearly simultaneous attack by many weapons on a big city or a rocket field would expose thousands of square kilometers to ignition. The distance across the ignition zone would in many cases be larger than the effective height of the atmosphere. This would change the nature of the winds produced by these fires, so that they might be more like those in severe thunderstorms or tornadoes than those of ordinary fires.

The fires would differ from most city and forest fires in having nobody to fight them. Except for Hiroshima and Nagasaki, the city fires of World War Two were mostly prevented from spreading by firefighters, who also play an essential role in keeping fires under control in peace-time. They would have no more effect in a thermonuclear war than an ant in a bonfire. So fires in cities and forests would be far more likely to spread than in peacetime or conventional wars.

A high density of ignition points leads to rapid burning. Where the number of established fires approached about one per building, the time of burning of the whole area would be comparable to the time to burn a single building, which is about half-an-hour to two hours for domestic buildings, and rather longer for most industrial and commercial buildings. The heat produced by such rapid burning around the centre of the ignition zone would inevitably produce high winds throughout the ignition zone, spreading the fires, and increasing the power of the fire still further. This is the mechanism of a firestorm: the development of a firestorm depends both on the size of the fire zone and on the density of combustible materials, not just on the latter, as is sometimes suggested.

The fires would also differ in many ways because of the effects of blast; in chapter 2 it is shown how blast would help fires to spread, make them more intense and increase the amount of material burnt.

In addition to the fires in cities and forests, there would also be fires – which might burn for months – in oil refineries, stocks of fuel and some of the 600,000 gas and oil wells in the world. In a summer war, extensive fires would rage in crops and in grasslands.

Experience with past fires is of limited use for understanding the bigger nuclear fires, but it is probably more reliable for the smaller ones. It might also help us to understand the spread of fires beyond the ignition zone, even in cities. In multiple attacks by nuclear weapons, the fires would spread into regions between ignition zones, and there might be other effects, which will be described in chapter 5.

Smoke

Light a wooden match and hold it just inside the edge of an upturned drinking glass. Some of the smoke goes into the air and some of it appears as a black smear on the glass — even a very fine layer of smoke cuts out a lot of light.

The individual particles of smoke on the glass, or in the air, cannot be seen because they are so small. Typically they are measured in microns (millionths of a meter), and they are often less than one micron across. It is because they are so black and so small that smoke is so effective in blocking out the light. The relatively large and light-coloured particles of dust thrown out from volcanoes or from craters of nuclear explosions are much less effective, by a factor of about ten (see appendix 3.1).

Imagine particles of smoke, like those on the glass, spread at random over everything on Earth between 30 and 70 degrees North, from the Gulf Coast of Texas or from Cairo in the south, to the north of Canada or Norway. Obviously it would stop much of the light of the Sun from reaching the leaves of plants. The same smoke would be at least as effective if it were spread out in a deep and uniform cloud high up in the atmosphere.

If a given amount of smoke cuts out 90 per cent of the light of a particular colour, then twice as much cuts out 99 per cent, three times as much cuts out 99.9 per cent and so on. This 'exponential' rule means that in some circumstances, a comparatively small increase or decrease in the amount of smoke can have profound consequences. Smoke particles that, when compressed together, would form a layer about two-fifths of a micron thick, are enough to cut out 90 per cent of sunlight, although there can be large variations depending on the burned material, the conditions of burning, and how quickly the smoke is diluted by being mixed with the air of the atmosphere.

How much smoke would be produced in a thermonuclear war? This is one of the more difficult things to find out, and, at the time that this is being written, is causing controversy. The mass of smoke produced by a fire varies from less than 1 per cent up to 20 per cent of the mass of the material burned; it depends on the nature of the material, how dry it is, whether the fire smoulders or flames, the temperature of burning, the oxygen supply, the wind conditions and the time since the fire started. Furthermore, the amount of smoke would depend on the scale of the war and the choice of targets; for forest fires it would also depend strongly on the weather and on the season of the year, as discussed in chapter 2.

However, the calculation given in box 3.1, which is like the original calculation of Crutzen and Birks, (note 1, chapter 1) shows that enough smoke could be produced to

Box 3.1

Smoke and Sunlight

This calculation shows that there could easily be enough smoke from the fires to cut out most of the sunlight from the Northern Hemisphere. We calculate the thickness of the cloud of smoke that would be made by burning a quarter of a million square kilometers (about 100,000 square miles) of built-up area of towns and cities, if the smoke were spread out uniformly over the whole Northern Hemisphere. This area is somewhat smaller than the area obtained in chapter 2 (p. 38), but like the other figures in the calculation, it is consistent with the recommended figures of the National Research Council Report (note 5, chapter 1).

The thickness of smoke over an area refers to the average thickness a cloud of smoke would have if the smoke in it were compressed to form a uniform solid layer. For simplicity it has been assumed that combustible materials and smoke both have an average density of 1 gram per cubic centimeter or 1,000 kilograms per cubic meter: this assumption does not affect the conclusions. The thickness is measured in microns, which are millionths of a meter.

Taking the average density of combustible materials in the fire areas as 4 grams per square centimeter, the average thickness of these materials is 4 centimeters, which is 40,000 microns. Only 75 per cent of this burns, just 4 per cent of the material burnt becomes smoke and only 50 per cent (conservatively) of the smoke survives after rising through the smoke plume. So if the smoke cloud were confined to the area of the fires, its average compressed thickness would be

40,000 micron $\times$ 0.75 $\times$ 0.04 $\times$ 0.5 = 600 micron

(continues)

> But the smoke is not confined to the fire area, it is spread out over the Hemisphere, which is 1,000 times larger, so the average thickness of the smoke is 0.6 micron. This is enough to reduce the sunlight reaching the ground by 97 per cent.[3]

darken a large fraction of the Earth's surface. Even on this evidence alone, the possibility of damaging the climate should not be ignored. Later we will show that the risks are substantial.

Some of the uncertainties can be reduced a little by comparing thermonuclear fires with past forest fires and the large fires of World War Two, but conditions then were not suitable for making precise observations. Smoke production in peacetime fires in towns has been studied because of its importance for fire safety, and smoke from forest fires has sometimes been dramatic, as described at the beginning of the next chapter. Such studies were used by TTAPS[4] and more recently by Crutzen, Galbally and Bruehl[5] to obtain their estimates of smoke production. The latter study suggests that petroleum products, such as fuel oil, asphalt and plastics, may be more important than wood in cities, because the smoke particles have more carbon in them, so they are blacker, and more effective in cutting out the heat of the Sun.

However, none of these studies has been able to deal adequately with the considerable differences, particularly in large cities, between fires started by thermonuclear weapons and previous fires. Because the combined size and power of the fires would be unprecedented, the conditions of burning would be very different from previous fires, with stronger winds of hotter air and regions of oxygen shortage that could be very large; these conditions might favour the production of large quantities of smoke. On the other hand smoke can burn, so if it were blown from one part of a fire into another it could be burned there.

Fires produce many things besides smoke. The major products are heat, carbon-dioxide gas and water vapour. The heat makes the air expand and rise, carrying the other materials high up in the atmosphere. This carbon dioxide and water vapour might produce significant effects locally, but the quantities would be small compared to the total amounts in the atmosphere, so their global effect is unlikely to be very significant by comparison with the effects of smoke and dust. Much of the water vapour would condense out as rain or snow, taking some of the smoke down with it. This is 'washout' and is described in the next chapter.

In addition all fires produce carbon monoxide, the killer gas of car exhausts. During the firestorms of World War Two in Germany, most of the people in shelters were probably killed by carbon-monoxide poisoning. For this reason, it is unlikely that people in shelters would survive a very large fire unless they had an independent air supply. Fires also produce oxides of nitrogen, which can affect the chemistry of the atmosphere.

Plastics are now widely used for fabrics, furnishings and other purposes, and relatively large amounts of poisonous gases are often produced when they burn. Also the accidents at Seveso and Bhopal remind us of the dangers of chemical release from industrial plant and stores, where dangerous materials are present on a scale far greater than many people realize. Furthermore rubbish and dust from blast damage, containing all kinds of materials, would be swept up by the fire winds.

The smoke and other pollutants would be carried in the fire plumes high up into the atmosphere. The duration of the nuclear winter depends on how high they go, and this depends on the atmosphere itself, the subject of the next section.

The Atmosphere

Life on Earth depends on the atmosphere. It provides the air that we breathe and protects us from extremes of heat and cold. It lets through enough sunlight for our crops to grow, but blocks out most of the dangerous ultraviolet light.

Human activity already affects the atmosphere. Smog and industrial smoke darken the sky and acid rain pollutes our lakes and forests. The removal of forests to provide agricultural land is believed to affect rainfall, and during this century the burning of coal and oil has been responsible for the great increase in carbon dioxide in the atmosphere.

But these effects are insignificant when compared with the sudden and drastic impact of the smoke and dust produced by a thermonuclear war.

Before we can say what such a war might do, we have to say something about what the atmosphere is like now. The air gets colder and thinner as you go higher, right out into space: that is why it is cold on mountains and why jet planes need to be pressurized. For most of the way the density goes down by about half for every 25,000 feet or 8 kilometers — jets often cruise at a height of about 8 kilometers.

But it only gets colder in the lower parts of the atmosphere up to about 33,000 feet or 10 kilometers, where it is about 60 or 70 degrees centigrade colder than at ground level — colder than a Siberian winter. The temperature then stops decreasing, and slowly rises again up to a height of about 30 miles or 50 kilometers. The height where the temperature 'pauses' is called the tropopause. Above this is the stratosphere and below it is the troposphere. These are shown in figure 3.2. The height of the tropopause varies with latitude; it is about 4 miles or 7 kilometers high at the poles and 10 miles or 16 kilometers high near the equator.

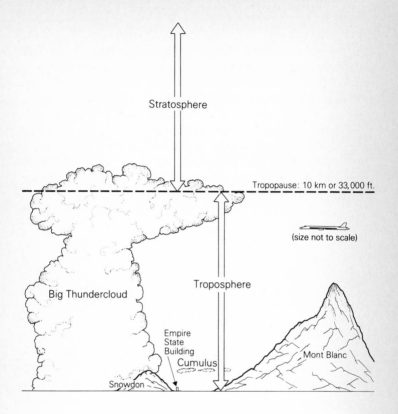

Figure 3.2. The normal atmosphere in temperature latitudes
Note: The temperature falls about 6.5°C for every kilometer or 3,300 feet up into the troposphere, but at the tropopause it stops falling, and in the stratosphere it slowly increases with height.
Scale: 5.3 centimeters equal to 33,000 feet (10 kilometers).

The troposphere is the part of the atmosphere that is familiar to us and it contains the weather and most of the clouds. Because of the warm air continually rising from the ground or the ocean, the troposphere is usually unstable and turbulent, particularly in the kilometer or two (a mile or so) nearest the ground. This turbulence stirs up the air. Within a couple of kilometers of the ground it usually takes about a day to stir it up, but higher up it takes longer, and nearer the tropopause it may take a week or a month. A lot depends on the weather: when there is a layer of air that is too warm for the air below it to rise, there is said to be an inversion, and humid air, fog or smog can hang around for days; on the other hand, when there is a thunderstorm, the air near the ground can be carried up to the tropopause in less than half-an-hour.

The stratosphere is like a permanent inversion and is quite different from the troposphere in many ways. It is made up of horizontal layers or 'strata' that do not mix much with each other or with the air of the troposphere. As a result small particles of volcanic dust, dust from nuclear explosions and possibly smoke from very large fires can remain in the stratosphere for months or even years.

There are often strong winds in the stratosphere, which can blow dust or smoke around the Earth in three weeks or less, so air and pollutants only 7 miles (11 kilometers) above our heads will usually go tens of thousands of miles around the world long before they fall to the ground!

The air of the atmosphere consists mainly of the gas nitrogen, but about one-fifth is the oxygen that is needed by most living things, and that is consumed in fires. There are much smaller quantities of water vapour, carbon dioxide and the inert gas argon, and tiny amounts of other gases. One of these is the ozone in the stratosphere, which is important despite its rarity, because it protects living things from some of the ultraviolet light of the Sun, known as UV-B, which we discuss in chapter 6.

Suppose there were a nuclear winter; then the darkness and cold would be caused by smoke and dust, and the higher they go, the longer they stay in the atmosphere and the worse the nuclear winter becomes. So it is important to know the height of the dusty mushroom clouds of the explosions and the smoke plumes of the fires.

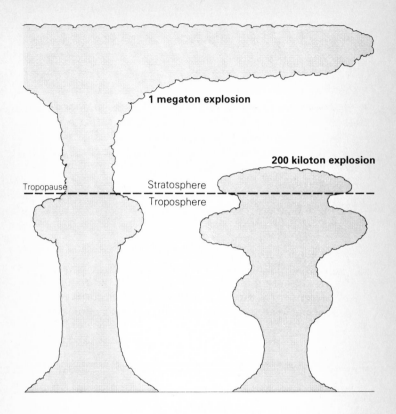

Figure 3.3. Approximate heights of thermonuclear explosion mushroom clouds

Note: Compare with the size of the mountains in figure 3.2. The larger weapons send most of their dust into the stratosphere, where it can stay for months.
Scale: 5.3 centimeters equal to 33,000 feet (10 kilometers), as in figure 3.2.

Mushroom Clouds and Smoke Plumes

Figure 3.3 shows the mushroom clouds from two thermo-nuclear explosions near the ground. The dust and radioactive fallout from the 200 kiloton (0.2 megaton)

Box 3.2

Height of Smoke from Fires

The height to which the smoke from fires rises depends mainly on the rate at which it produces heat, that is its power, w. The theory and comparison with observations of forest fires, a city fire and volcanoes are presented by Manins, who gives the approximate formulae

Top $= 0.25$ w$^{1/4}$
Base $= 0.15$ w$^{1/4}$

where heights are measured in kilometers and power in megawatts.[6] The formulae are adequate for heights in the troposphere under average conditions, but require adjustment for estimating heights in the stratosphere. The formulae are discussed and applied to examples in appendix 3.3.

explosion are carried by the cloud into the middle to upper troposphere, so they fall to the ground, or are washed out by rain or snow, within a few days to a month or so. But the 1 megaton explosion is 5 times more energetic and most of the material from the mushroom cloud goes into the stratosphere, where the finer dust stays for many months or even a year or two (see appendix 3.2).

The heat from fires, volcanoes and even thunderstorms sends the air and plumes of smoke, dust or water vapour high up into the atmosphere. Usually the more powerful the source of heat, the more the air is heated and the higher it goes. The power of the heat source is the rate at which it produces heat. The heat of fires comes from burning wood or other combustible material, the heat of volcanoes from the interior of the Earth and the heat in thunderstorms, surprisingly, from the condensation of water in humid air. The height of the plumes also depends on the weather and the amount of mixing with cooler air on the way up.

But despite these complications the fairly simple formula of box 3.2 gives a good idea of the height of smoke for a wide range of different events, from the eruption of volcanoes to large forest fires. To calculate the height reached by the smoke from a large fire, we need to know its power, and the formula then tells us how high the smoke is likely to go. Details of the calculation and two examples are given in appendix 3.3, and smoke plumes from two possible nuclear city fires are illustrated in figure 3.4. Because fires started by nuclear weapons are ignited almost simultaneously over a wide area, they are

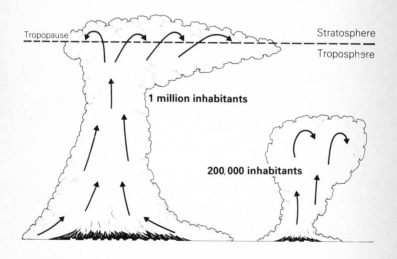

Figure 3.4. Approximate heights of smoke plumes of city fires ignited by thermonuclear weapons
Scale: 5.3 centimeters equal to 33,000 feet (10 kilometers), as in figures 3.2 and 3.3.

likely to burn more quickly than natural forest fires or the fires of World War Two, and the smoke would go correspondingly higher. Nevertheless TTAPS and other authors have not taken this possibility into account in their scenarios. They assume conservatively that most of the smoke would go into the troposphere, with a small proportion from fiercely burning firestorms going into the lower stratosphere.

These are the local effects of nuclear fires. Their scale could be so large and their number so great that they could produce major changes in the atmosphere of the Northern Hemisphere, or even the whole Earth. That is the subject of the next chapter.

4   War on the Atmosphere

The Smoke Spreads — Twilight at Noon

During the last ten days of September 1950, over a hundred fires burned in the forests of western Canada.[1] A great pall of smoke spread over much of Canada and the eastern coast of the USA, as shown in figure 4.1, and even as far as western Europe. In many places the smoke was so dense that the Sun could be looked at directly without discomfort. Most of the smoke was between 10,000 and 16,000 feet high (3–5 kilometers) and took about a week or ten days to reach England, France, Denmark and Switzerland, a third of the way round the world from the fires, by which time it had risen as high as 23,000 feet (7 kilometers).

The dust from the eruption of the El Chichon volcano in Mexico in 1982 went into the stratosphere, and formed a continuous band around the Earth within three weeks of its first appearance. The dust from the Mount St Helen's eruption in the north-west of the USA reached the middle troposphere. This dust cloud darkened the sky, and, according to careful estimates, it caused the daytime temperature beneath it to drop by 5–8 degrees centigrade (5°C–8°C).[2]

The speed of the wind generally increases with height up to the tropopause, where it can blow at more than a

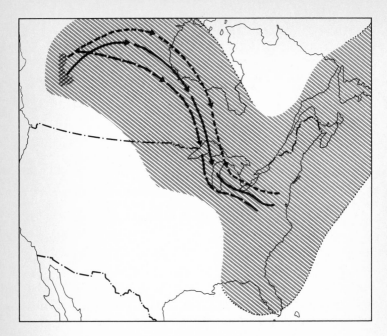

Figure 4.1. Smoke from the Canadian forest fires of September
1950[1]

Note: The small darkened areas represent the fires, and the shading shows
where smoke was observed, although it does not include observations in
Western Europe.

hundred miles an hour. Usually its direction changes too,
and these changes are known as wind shear. Because of
wind shear, a tall cloud can be blown in different
directions at different heights, so that the cloud increases
its area. The clouds of smoke and dust produced in a
nuclear war would spread out and cover larger and larger
areas of the World, dimming the light of the Sun. But at
the same time the density of the smoke or dust would be
decreased.

What would happen after a large-scale nuclear war?
Suppose the war was like the one described in chapter 2.

Suppose that the attack were during the day in Western Europe; the first megaton groundburst explosions would send clouds of radioactive dust into the stratosphere, and the smaller groundbursts would send it into the troposphere. During the first hour, the city fires would begin to burn, sending their smoke to all heights up to the lower stratosphere, with the most intense city fires sending their plumes of smoke to the greatest heights. Fuel stocks, including coal, oil and gas would burn too, as would the drier forest and grasslands within the ignition zones of the explosions. Exactly how long the fires would burn, and how far they would spread, is difficult to say, but it would be from hours to weeks.

After the explosions, and as the fires burned, the clouds of smoke would drift downwind, spreading outwards as they went. At first, near the fires, they would be so dense that the sunlight would be reduced to darkness, except for the light of the fires. They would drift hundreds of miles in hours and thousands of miles around the world in a week or two. After a few days the sunlight might begin to penetrate through, but only enough to raise the level of illumination to that of moonlight or twilight. Within a week or two, one could expect a continuous band of smoke and dust around the world, mostly between the latitudes 30 and 70 degrees North, where most of the World's population lives and where most of our crops are grown. By then it might be like twilight or a heavily overcast day, even at noon.

The edges of the smoke and dust would be patchy and irregular, and they would spread to the north and to the south, possibly as occasional streamers.

The TTAPS group of scientists, whom we mentioned in the introduction, were the first to make detailed studies of the effects of the dust and smoke on the atmosphere (note 2, chapter 1). Among them were planetary physicists who had made a study of dust storms on Mars. It had been observed that during a dust storm in one hemisphere of Mars, the pattern of the winds would change, blowing dust into the other hemisphere. They suggested, by analogy, that something similar might happen on Earth after a nuclear war. Normally the atmospheric circulations in the Northern and Southern Hemispheres are fairly independent except at very great heights, and it may take a year or more for volcanic dust from a large volcanic explosion like Krakatoa in the Southern Hemisphere to reach Europe or America. But after a nuclear war, the circulation might be so changed, because of the heating of the clouds of smoke and dust by the Sun, that they could be carried across the equator and into the Southern Hemisphere within a month or two. Computer calculations, whose results are illustrated in appendix 4.1, tend to confirm this.

Sunlight and Infra-Red Radiation

Sunny days are usually warmer than cloudy days, but clear winter nights are cold and cloudy summer nights can be uncomfortably hot. The smoke and dust of a nuclear war would stay in the atmosphere for many days and nights, and it is not immediately obvious what this would do to the temperature.

The Earth is kept warm by heat which comes from the light of the Sun. Some of this light is visible white light, made by mixing the colours of the rainbow, from the short wavelength violet to the long wavelength red. But there is also sunlight which is invisible to our eyes; some being untraviolet radiation with wavelengths somewhat shorter than violet, and some being infra-red radiation with wavelengths somewhat longer than red.

But the Earth does not go on getting hotter and hotter as it gets more and more heat from the Sun. Somehow it loses the heat that it gains, so that it reaches a balance at the temperatures which we experience in our daily lives. It does this by giving off invisible 'earthlight' of its own, which is infra-red radiation with wavelengths about twenty times longer than a typical wavelength of visible light — much longer than for almost any of the radiation from the Sun.

The Sun looks white-hot, and so it is — at nearly 6000°C. We cannot look at the Earth from space — but we can observe it with infra-red cameras, and it appears to be 'infra-red hot', but at a temperature as low as −18°C! Obviously this is not 'hot' in any ordinary sense of the word: it is a typical January temperature for northern Canada or Siberia, and is certainly not a typical average temperature for the surface of the Earth, which is a comfortable 13°C. So what is wrong?

The answer is that most of the infra-red radiation that goes into space does not come from the surface of the Earth, but from the atmosphere, at various heights whose temperature averages about −18°C. The surface of the Earth receives a lot of direct sunlight, and it then gives off infra-red radiation of its own, but most of this cannot escape directly into space because it is trapped by the clouds, the water vapour and the carbon dioxide in the atmosphere. These are like a blanket that hinders the escape of heat from the surface of the Earth, and keeps us warm. The blanket itself is much cooler than the surface, and it is this that can be seen from space. This is the 'greenhouse effect' and keeps us about 31°C warmer on average than we would otherwise be, as much as the difference between summer and winter temperatures in a continental climate.

The greenhouse effect only works because sunlight can penetrate through the atmosphere to the surface of the Earth much more easily than infra-red radiation from the Earth can get out again.

Unlike water and carbon dioxide, smoke blocks out sunlight, but lets most of the infra-red radiation through; this was observed after the Canadian forest fire described at the beginning of this chapter. So thick clouds of smoke would stop most of the sunlight warming the Earth, but would allow most of the infra-red radiation to escape. They could stop the greenhouse effect from working or even put it into reverse, with smoke clouds near the tropopause being warmer than the land below. This would completely change our atmosphere, which could become at least a temporary victim of a thermonuclear war.

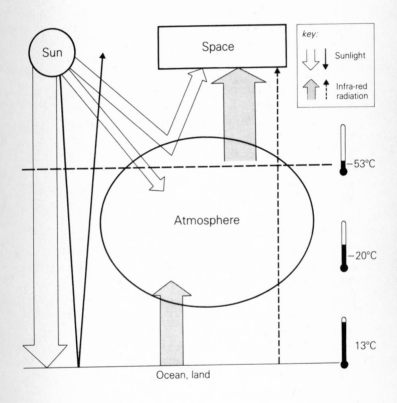

Figure 4.2. Sketch of net transfer of heat between the Sun, the atmosphere, the surface of the Earth and Space under normal conditions, with a strong greenhouse effect

Note: The bulk of the atmosphere is much colder than the surface of the Earth.

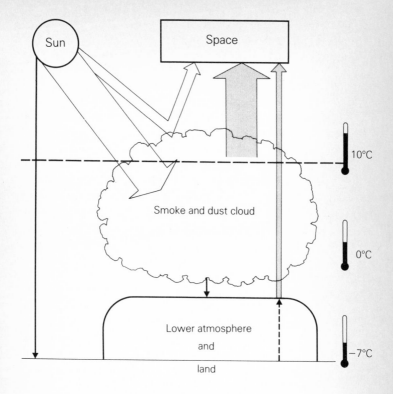

Figure 4.3. Sketch of approximate net heat transfer over land when the Earth is covered by a cloud of smoke and dust

Note: The upper atmosphere is much warmer and the Earth is much cooler than normal. The comparison with the previous sketch is not precise, because the atmosphere after a nuclear war does not settle down even approximately to a steady state, but the main changes are illustrated.

A thermonuclear war would affect the temperature of the Earth in many other ways, although probably none would be so great as the removal or reversal of the greenhouse effect. Some of these effects are shown in figures 4.2 and 4.3. Normally much of the Earth is covered by clouds which reflect some of the sunlight back into space. The relatively dark dust and even darker smoke would reflect less of the sunlight, and this would tend to make the Earth a bit warmer. Also the fires and some of the explosions would send water and carbon dioxide up into the atmosphere, with effects that are described in chapter 5. The heat from the fires themselves would raise local temperatures temporarily, but on a global scale this effect is negligible when compared with the heat that we receive from the Sun.

The combination of all these effects is complicated, but detailed computer calculations all suggest that if the smoke and dust were to rise above the lower levels of the troposphere, there would be an overall drastic cooling of the surface of the Earth. In a summer war, the cooling on land would be comparable to the difference between a normal summer and winter. At present it appears that this change would, on average, be somewhat less than the difference between a normal July and a normal January for temperate climates like Europe and the USA, but it would be greater than the usual temperature differences in subtropical and tropical climates.

Figure 4.4 shows how the temperature could change in the weeks and months following a large-scale nuclear war. It is adapted from TTAPS (note 2, chapter 1) to take into account the effect of the oceans.[3] The principal graph is used for our baseline scenario and shows an average temperature over the land in the Northern Hemisphere after the June war described in chapter 2. This average temperature drops by a maximum of 19°C, but between 30 degrees North and 60 degrees North the average would be about 26°C, and there would be very large local fluctuations about the average. For comparison, the average normal temperature difference between June and January in the UK is about 10°C.

Very large volcanic eruptions in the past have been followed by global cooling of about 0.5–1°C, and severe crop failure and famines followed some of the largest eruptions between 1750 and 1900. The drop in tempera-

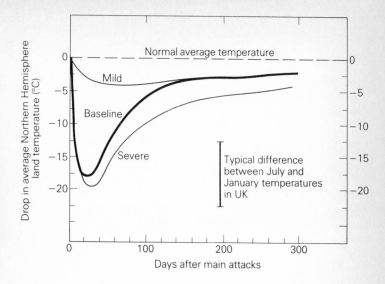

Figure 4.4. Expected variation in average land temperature in the Northern Hemisphere after a large-scale nuclear exchange

Notes: a) The principal curve is for our baseline scenario, which follows the TTAPS baseline scenario, but scales down the temperature decrease to take into account the effect of the oceans, following the calculations of Thompson et al. (note 3, chapter 4).

b) The 'mild' curve is for the effect of dust alone, similarly scaled. It corresponds to the effect of a summer war without smoke, so it is more severe than the 'mild' winter scenario at the end of the next chapter.

c) The 'severe' curve refers to a 10,000 megaton exchange and also includes more severe assumptions about the production and lifetime of smoke and dust; it was used as a basis for the biological assessment by Ehrlich et al. (note 3, chapter 1). Our own severe scenario would have a similar temperature drop, but would take much longer to return to normal: this is principally because we have included the effect of the postnuclear depression of the tropopause.

ture was generally less than one-twentieth of what might be expected after a large-scale nuclear war.

The ocean has a moderating effect on climate, and countries like the UK that lie by the borders of continents have a climate that is generally far less extreme than continental areas like the mid-west of the USA and almost all of the USSR. The normal winters in the UK are much less severe than at similar latitudes in these continental areas. This is because the oceans retain much more heat than the land, and so they are less influenced by changes in the heat from the Sun. But the winters in countries like the UK tend to be more stormy, and to have more rapid temperature changes from day to day and from week to week.

All this would probably be true of the nuclear winter too: the oceans would retain much of their heat and so reduce the overall effect of a nuclear winter, particularly near coasts. On the other hand, after a spring or summer war, the temperature contrast between land and sea would be greater than for a normal winter, so the storms, winds and sudden changes in temperature could all be more severe.

In order to calculate the effects of the oceans and the differing effects of a nuclear war on the climate in different parts of the world, very large computer calculations are needed, which require big computers. The National Center for Atmospheric Research in Colorado in western USA (NCAR) has some of the best computers in the world. Covey, Schneider and Thompson were atmospheric scientists from this research centre who carried out the calculations that were used as the basis for figure 4.5, showing the calculated changes in temperature in the Northern Hemisphere ten days after the beginning of a large-scale nuclear war in Spring or Summer.

In order to simplify their calculations, the NCAR scientists assumed that the oceans would not cool. But in fact they would cool, though more slowly and less severely than the land, and they would then retain lower temperatures for several years. Ice in the sea and snow on land would also influence the nuclear winter. These effects are also produced by large volcanic eruptions, which can be used as a guide to the effects of a nuclear war, as shown in box 4.1.

Near the edges of the cloud of smoke and dust, and in

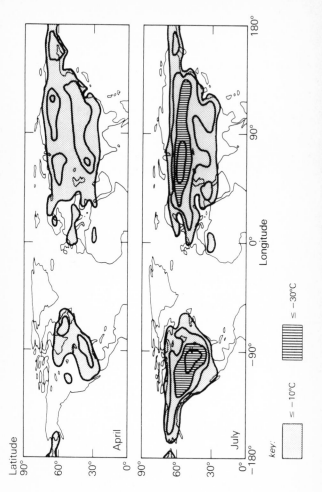

Figure 4.5. Average surface temperatures 10 days after a large-scale nuclear war in April or in July

Note: After Thompson et al. (note 3, chapter 4).

Box 4.1

Volcanoes and Extended Climatic Effects

The largest volcanic eruptions send enough dust into the atmosphere to have a significant effect on the Earth's climate.[4] Averaging over many eruptions during the last century, the temperature is observed to drop by roughly 0.5–1°C, with a delay of about a year for effects of Southern Hemisphere eruptions in the Northern Hemisphere, and detectable effects over about 3 years. The size and extended period of time could be caused by a combination of:

1. Long residence time of the dust in the stratosphere.
2. Slow cooling of the sea under the dust cloud. This in its turn cools the atmosphere when the dust cloud clears.
3. Increased sea ice, which hinders the warming of the atmosphere by the seas.
4. Increased snow cover, which reflects more sunlight when the dust clears.

The first cause does not appear to be enough to explain the observed effects, but the remainder would also operate after a nuclear war. These are called 'climatic feedback effects', and they might be expected to extend the climatic effects of a nuclear war for a few years. Robock has modelled these climatic effects both for volcanoes and for a nuclear war, using a relatively simple climatic model, and has obtained results for the former which are reasonably consistent with observation.[5]

On the basis of the evidence from volcanoes that the feedback effects are significant, we introduce a relatively small drop in temperature over a period of three years into the climatic effects of the nuclear war, as described in the last section of this chapter.

the early days when the clouds were patchy, there would be sudden changes in temperature. This would probably happen in many tropical and subtropical regions, which do not normally experience very low temperatures at all. The changed pattern of winds could also have serious effects on local climates.

All these climatic changes would have serious consequences for life, particularly agriculture, and these consequences are considered in detail in chapters 6 and 7. Agriculture is also very dependent on rainfall, which is notoriously difficult to predict, even in normal circumstances. But the calculations of the NCAR scientists suggest that a few weeks after a large-scale nuclear war, the reduced sunlight would result in reduced evaporation, fewer rain or snow clouds below the dust and smoke, and so less precipitation, especially inland.

Fallout and Pollution

Smoke and dust that are sent into the atmosphere eventually come down again, but it can take from minutes to years to do so; the time that it takes depends crucially on how high it goes.

If we look towards a distant horizon after rain or snow, we can see much further than usual, particularly near cities. This is because of a natural cleaning effect — the dust, smoke and other pollutants stick to the raindrops and snowflakes, and fall to the ground with them. If rain falls on our windows or car windscreens, we may find that the dirt has been washed onto them, and dirty snow is a common sight near northern industrial cities.

A few minutes after a groundburst nuclear explosion or the development of a large fire, some of the dust or smoke would be washed to the ground. The explosions and the fires would take large quantities of water into the atmosphere with the dust and the smoke, and this would condense into raindrops, falling as 'black rain'. This fell in

Hiroshima and after some of the Pacific nuclear weapons tests. Although there is evidence from many sources that this early removal by rain is not very efficient, we follow the NRC Report in assuming that 50 per cent of the smoke is removed in the plume and returns to Earth as rain.[6]

Groundburst explosions produce dust of all sizes, and lumps of material, some of which fall to the ground within seconds or minutes by their own weight, causing the intense radioactivity known as early fallout, that is so damaging to living things. But as we saw in the last chapter, most of the smoke is made of particles less than a micron across, which cannot fall to the ground so quickly.

The less intense fires and the nuclear explosions of less than about half a megaton would send most of their smoke and dust into the troposphere, from where they would eventually be washed to the ground by rain or snow, or drift down through the turbulent lower atmosphere. Typically this would take an average of a few days for the lower troposphere, to a few weeks or months for the upper troposphere, as indicated in chapter 3.

It is probable that the layer of smoke and dust would cause an inversion in the upper layers of the troposphere, lowering the tropopause by a few kilometers, so that the 'postnuclear troposphere' would be shallower and the 'postnuclear stratosphere' would reach closer to the ground. In that case the proportion of smoke and dust in the postnuclear stratosphere would be increased very significantly.

The more intense fires and the bigger nuclear explosions would send a significant fraction of their smoke and dust, possibly most of it, into the postnuclear stratosphere, where it could remain for months and even years. The uncertainties in the time that this smoke and dust would stay in the atmosphere are discussed in the next chapter.

As the atmosphere clears, the sunlight comes through, and the climate would probably, though not certainly, return slowly to normal, with some disturbances lasting for many years.

But the return to Earth of the dust, the smoke and the other prodcuts of combustion would have further very damaging effects.

The dust from the groundburst nuclear explosions is radioactive, and this radioactivity slowly decays. That is one of the reasons why the early fallout near an explosion is so much worse than the global fallout that reaches the ground much later. The megaton weapons send their radioactive dust into the stratosphere and most of the radioactivity is lost before it reaches the ground. But there are many fractional megaton weapons in MIRVS and cruise missiles (see chapter 2), which send their dust into the troposphere, from where it can be washed out in days to weeks. This produces the so-called 'intermediate' fallout whose importance has been emphasized by the TTAPS group (see appendix 4.2).

Smoke and other products of combustion are notorious for their pollution, and this will be discussed in chapters 6 and 7 on the biological effects of a nuclear winter.

One further hazard remains to be discussed in this section: the nitrogen oxides from the explosions and the fires could interact with the ozone in the stratosphere, destroying some of it and letting more of the dangerous ultraviolet radiation through to the surface of the Earth. The amount getting through could be more than doubled.

Nuclear Winter Scenarios

The nuclear winter predictions depend on several different fields of science and various scientific methods. Simple calculations like those in the original paper of Crutzen and Birks have been followed by much more elaborate computer models, like those of the TTAPS and NCAR groups (chapter 1, *passim*). These are necessary because the processes are complicated. The computer models do not provide exact predictions, but they help us to assess the risks. Their reliability can be judged to a limited extent by using the same model to study both the nuclear winter and some observed natural phenomenon, like cooling due to volcanic dust in the atmosphere. All of the models used so far for the nuclear winter are adaptations of models used for other purposes.

The results from the different models are not always the same, but this is not surprising, as they have been designed to do different jobs. Each model gives a more accurate picture of some aspects of the nuclear winter, and a less accurate picture of others, so that best picture is made up of bits from each of them. However there remain many uncertainties, which we discuss in the next chapter.

In this section we describe some specific nuclear winter research, which leads in the next section to a description of the postnuclear atmosphere that is used in the biological chapters.

Crutzen and Birks are atmospheric chemists who were commissioned by the Royal Swedish Academy of Sciences to write an article on global atmospheric effects of nuclear war, when these were believed to be primarily chemical in nature. They carried out the pioneering calculations on the darkness produced by large quantities of smoke, but they had to meet a publication deadline, and were not able to go into detail (see note 1, chapter 1).

The TTAPS group are planetary scientists who specialize in the study of planetary atmospheres, including the pollution of the Earth's atmosphere. They began their work with a study of the effects of the dust from explosions, but on learning of the work of Crutzen and Birks, they included the smoke as well (note 2, chapter 1). Their results have been used for much of the research into the long-term global biological effects of nuclear war, and have stimulated much recent research on the atmospheric effects too.

In the TTAPS model averages are taken over the whole

hemisphere and over all seasons, and detailed calculations are made for the effects of smoke and dust on the atmosphere at different heights. Because it looks at only one dimension, the height, it is known as a one-dimensional model. The model includes both dust and smoke, with only a little smoke in the stratosphere; the effects of coagulation and settling by gravity are included, and detailed calculations are made of the effect on visible and infra-red light. Both the reduction in sunlight and the changes in temperature are followed over several months. As the authors point out, the moderating effect of the oceans was not included in the main calculations, nor is it included in the graphs of the temperature, so the papers need to be read with care.

Clearly, averages over the Hemisphere leave out many important effects, and some of these were taken into account in subsequent two-dimensional models, that include the dependence on latitude, and three-dimensional models that take into account the longitude as well. The price paid for having more dimensions is that less detail can be represented. Many different models and calculations are needed to help us understand the atmospheric consequences of nuclear war.

MacCracken is a scientist at the Lawrence Livermore National Laboratory in California, a laboratory which primarily carries out weapons research for the US Government. He started with a one-dimensional model, that gave results that were broadly in agreement with those of the TTAPS group. He then used two- and three-dimensional models to represent the winds and the horizontal movement of the smoke, together with the effect of the oceans on the temperature, of the clouds on the light, and of rain and snow on the washout of the smoke.[7] No effects of wind shear were included, and the attacks were all supposed to be concentrated in three very localized regions, so the patchiness of the smoke clouds was exaggerated. As a result rather large areas of the Hemisphere were missed by the clouds and the maximum average drop in temperature was smaller — only 11°C for the latitudes between 30 degrees and 60 degrees North. Nevertheless, even this drop in temperature would be an unprecedented climatic catastrophe.

The work of Covey and his colleages at NCAR was discussed earlier in this chapter (p. 66).[8] They used a three-dimensional model, with much more detailed dependence on height. They calculated the effect on the temperature and the winds, which they found were modified enough to produce significant transport of smoke to the Southern Hemisphere, but unfortunately they were not able to put this effect into their detailed calculations. They assumed an initial concentration of smoke that was uniformly distributed between 27 degrees North and 71 degrees North and between ground level and 10 kilometers, and they neglected dust. They found temperature reductions intermediate between those of TTAPS and those of MacCracken.

At the Computing Centre of the USSR Academy of Sciences in Moscow, Aleksandrov and Stenchikov used similar computer models to MacCracken, but made more severe assumptions as to the amount and distribution of the smoke.[9] These results are discussed and compared with some of the American work in a later joint paper (see note 3, chapter 4), that also gives more detail on seasonal differences, and which we use in figure 4.5.

Official organizations became aware of the research on the nuclear winter at an early stage. In early 1983 the US Department of Defense asked the National Research Council (NRC) of the US National Academy of Sciences to assess the possible atmospheric effects of nuclear war, and a committee of specialists was set up. They reported in early 1985, summarized much of the earlier work, which they carefully assessed, and provided baseline scenarios of their own (see note 5, chapter 1). Their conclusions are given in box 4.2, and their baseline scenario is used as a basis for many of the atmospheric effects described in this book (see note 5, chapter 1).

Box 4.2

Conclusions of the 1985 US National Research Council Report

'The general conclusion that the committee draws from this study is the following: a major nuclear exchange would insert significant amounts of smoke, fine dust, and undesirable chemical species into the atmosphere. These depositions could result in dramatic perturbations of the atmosphere lasting over a period of at least a few weeks. Estimation of the amounts, the vertical distributions, and the subsequent fates of these materials involves large uncertainties. Furthermore, accurate, detailed accounts of the response of the atmosphere, the redistribution and removal of the depositions, and the duration of a greatly degraded environment lie beyond the present state of knowledge.

Nevertheless, the committee finds that, unless one or more of the effects lie near the less severe end of their uncertainty ranges, or unless some mitigating effect has been overlooked, there is a clear possibility that great portions of the land areas of the northern temperate zone (and, perhaps, a larger segment of the planet) could be severely affected. Possible impacts include major temperature reductions (particularly for an exchange that occurs in the summer) lasting for weeks, with subnormal temperatures persisting for months. The impact of these temperature reductions and associated meteorological changes on the surviving population, and on the biosphere that supports the survivors, could be severe, and deserves careful independent study.'

In September 1982 the International Council of Scientific Unions adopted a resolution at its nineteenth General Assembly to make an assessment of the biological, medical and physical effects of the large-scale use of nuclear weapons, and the international ENUWAR committee was set up in 1983 to investigate these effects, Sir Frederick Warner of the British Royal Society as chairman (see note 6, chapter 1). They have organized a large number of international scientific workshops 'to focus sharply on establishing the reality or illusion of long-term global climatic and biological effects of several scenarios and nuclear exchanges'.[10] They have succeeded in aiding and encouraging many scientists of different countries and different branches of science, including two of the authors of this book, to focus their attention on the global effects of nuclear war. They are due to report in the late Summer of 1985.

The Postnuclear Atmosphere

Much of the scientific research is in technical jargon and is not easy for the layman to follow or interpret. Here we give an account of the likely consequences of the June war described in chapter 2, according to the present evidence. The effect on sunlight has been described earlier in the chapter (p. 59), so we concentrate on the cold. This would vary from country to country, as it does for an ordinary winter, which is almost certainly our best guide: both a nuclear winter and an ordinary winter are caused by less sunlight reaching the surface of the Earth. There are also important differences, but the computer models help us to understand them.

This is our scenario: after the initial attack, the temperature would start to drop steadily below the spreading clouds of smoke and dust. The clouds would cover most of the USA, Europe and the USSR, and by the end of a week almost all the land area in latitudes between Texas or north Africa and northern Canada or Norway would be involved. By the middle of July average temperatures in this area would be at their lowest. In the Mediterranean countries, the northern USA, Japan and much of China this would be comparable to normal January temperatures, whereas further north, in Canada, northern Europe and the USSR, the average temperature would be slightly higher than a normal January, and further South it would be lower.

In the following weeks the smoke and dust would drift north and south, with streamers hundreds of miles across reaching through subtropical and tropical regions across the Equator, sending their temperatures down by 3–10°C in continental interiors, and rather less near coasts (see note 4, chapter 4). At all latitudes near coasts and near the edges of the clouds there would be severe wind storms, with resulting fluctuations in temperature as the clouds came and went and the wind changed in strength or direction. These fluctuations might reach 5–10°C.

In the UK the temperature would be expected to go down to average December temperatures, with fluctuations between a cool summer and an exceptionally severe winter, as the gale-force winds changed from west to east and back again.

In the Northern Hemisphere the temperature would rise a few degrees in August and September, but the following winter would be 3–4°C colder than normal. The following Summer would be cooler by about 2°C, and would stay 1°C below normal for two years.

Far from the streamers in the southern parts of South America, Africa and Australia, there would be some decrease in sunlight starting a few weeks or months after the attack, with temperature drops of about 1°C during the year following the war. Local attacks on military targets would produce darkness and cooling for a few weeks in some downwind areas.

This is our baseline scenario. Like others, it required an assessment of the likely consequences on the evidence available, and, like them, it is subject to uncertainties. These are discussed in detail in the next chapter.

5 Uncertainties and Risks

Introduction

In practice the climatic consequences of a thermonuclear war can't be predicted accurately; the research can only help us to evaluate the risks. But how is it possible to do even this, when the weather can't be predicted with any confidence for more than a few days at most?

The main reason is that average temperatures, like the difference between an ordinary summer and winter, depend on well-known properties of heat and light, but the daily and weekly changes in the weather depend on the dynamics of a turbulent fluid (air) on a rotating Earth, which is much more difficult to understand. The climate is easier to predict than the weather.

While the risk of nuclear war remains, there is a need for a continuous reassessment of its consequences. The variety of possible consequences is great, both because of the range of possible wars and because of incomplete understanding of the processes involved.

The early research has had to rely heavily on comparisons with other processes and events such as the fires of World War Two, volcanic eruptions, natural forest fires, normal atmospheric circulation and climatic change. It also has had to depend on the methods developed for the study of these phenomena. These analogies and methods are of limited use because of the unique character of thermonuclear war, and new methods are being developed which take account of this.

The global consequences result from sequences of processes. At present, the main sequence is believed to be

Nuclear explosions → fires → smoke → blocking of sunlight → darkness and cold at the Earth's surface

Each stage depends on the one before, and uncertainties early in the sequence propagate down it. The processes are complicated, but they can be modelled using computers. These computer models help us to understand what might happen, but they are not sufficiently sophisticated to distinguish all the possibilities, and this is likely to be so for many years. Similar computer models are used to study past events like those mentioned above, and they can be checked against observation and later modified to take account of the differences between theory and observation. For obvious reasons, this is not possible for the unique aspects of a large-scale nuclear war. That is why uncertainties will remain, despite the development of new methods.

The scientific study of the global consequences of nuclear war provides us with few certainties, but it can tell us about the likely risks involved. This chapter gives an account of the uncertainties and risks as they appear from the results of current research available to the authors. Inevitably, the assessment of the risks will change as further research is done. The direction of this change might be towards milder or more severe global consequences, lesser or greater risks.

The discussion of uncertainties that follows is fairly technical, but much of the information that it contains is summed up in the final section of this chapter, which shows the enormous range of severity in the possible effects.

Uncertainties

The estimates of risk depend on understanding the uncertainties, of which there are many. The following list, classifies a number of them.

1 *Fire: ignition* The ignition of fires depends on the thermal effects of nuclear weapons, which have been observed in nuclear weapons tests above ground, and in the attacks on Hiroshima and Nagasaki. The results are summarized in chapter 2, but the conditions in the tests, which were largely in deserts or near islands, were very different from those to be expected in a thermonuclear war. In particular, industrial haze is likely to reduce the area of ignition in cities, and cloudy conditions would sometimes reduce it for airbursts. But, conversely, cloudy conditions could increase ignition area significantly for low airbursts and ground-bursts, particularly in cities if the ground is covered in snow. If nearby explosions are separated in time by more than a few seconds, then the heat from the later one could be partially absorbed by material produced by the earlier one.

2 *Fire: effect of blast* This is discussed in chapter 2. In towns and cities, blast can start fires, but it can also blow out small isolated flames. Modern building methods and materials are very different from those of World War Two, so it is difficult to predict what would happen to the combustible office materials of the very common commercial steel and glass skyscrapers, for example. The character of the fires in both cites and forests is likely to change in each of a sequence of regions radiating from the nuclear explosion; each region needs to be studied.

3 *Combustible materials* It is necessary to take into

account the very large geographical differences in the amount of wood used in building. Some of the city fires might be sufficiently hot to burn aluminium and other materials not normally considered to be combustible.

4 *Fire structure* Only from Hiroshima and Nagasaki do we have direct evidence of the effect of a large density of ignition points, but the areas of about 4 square miles (10 square kilometers) were small compared to the hundreds of square miles that would be common in large cities attacked by thermonuclear weapons. Computer models of large fires have been reported (see note 6, chapter 3), but there is a need to include important feedback processes. The winds produced by fires themselves help to determine the rate of burning and spread of the fires, and would produce many of the effects given in the section on blast in chapter 2. For a given initial surface density of fuel and ignition points, the large fires produce stronger winds, higher central temperature, greater shortage of oxygen, and a greater effect of vorticity (swirling winds). All of these affect the fire itself, particularly its rate of burning and thus its power. The power in turn affects the height of the plume, which determines the equilibrium height of the smoke, which is crucial to its influence on the climate. At present, there does not appear to be agreement as to whether a typical burning rate in cities might be 1 or 10 kilograms per square meter per hour, and it could easily vary within this range.

5 *Very large fires* Evidence from thunderstorms suggests that when a source of heat is large compared to the height of the atmosphere, plumes appear about 20 kilometers apart. Thus for large cities or dry forests there would be many plumes. Under these conditions down-drafts would become important, with relatively dry warm air feeding into the fire, helping to spread it and increasing the height of the plume. Fire spread is

difficult to estimate; swirling fires, in which fire is spread by a moving vortex of hot air, need to be investigated to determine whether they could be significant.

6 *Smoke properties* We do not know how much smoke would be produced in very large and rapidly burning fires, with high winds near the edge, intense heat and probable shortage of oxygen near the centre and very rapid cooling in the updrafts. Certainly simple analogies with past fires are inadequate, and an understanding of the principal features of the physics and chemistry of smoke formation is required. Smoke from the edge may be burned near the centre, and smoke from some fires may be burned in others, or by other thermonuclear explosions. Under an electron microscope, smoke is seen to be made up of large numbers of small particles about one-hundredth to one-tenth of a micron across, stuck to one another in sparse clusters shaped like the gnarled branches of an old tree. The usual theories of smoke coagulation and its optical properties assume that it grows into large and larger solid spheres, but this is a very crude approximation. Mountain and Mulholland[1] have shown that the sparse clusters coagulate more rapidly than solid spheres, and others are investigating their optical properties: the required modifications of the usual theories are large, and the same applies to the rate of settling, which is much slower for a sparse cluster than for a solid sphere. Such modifications could greatly extend the effect of smoke in the postnuclear stratosphere.

7 *Chemistry of smoke* The chemistry of volcanic dust determines its climatic impact; the chemistry of smoke in the stratosphere could be just as important, and it has hardly been studied. The destruction of smoke by atmospheric ozone appears to be difficult to determine. Carbon is an excellent catalyst, so the smoke could

catalyse the destruction of ozone and many other chemical reactions, substantially changing the chemistry of the upper atmosphere around it. The large surface area of sparse clusters would increase these effects, but the coating of the smoke particles by impurities could decrease them, just as industrial catalysts are 'poisoned'.

8 *Water* Most of the effects of water make the climatic effects less severe. Wet weather beforehand, particularly in forests and grasslands, reduces the probability of ignition and spread to near zero in many cases. Water vapour is produced in fires, but most of the water in the fire plume could be entrained from the water vapour or droplets in the surrounding air. Condensation in the plume produces 'black rain', which is believed to be an inefficient removal process for observed fires, but could be significantly more or less efficient for the nuclear fires. The energy released by condensation would cause the plume to rise higher, but the water accompanying the smoke into the upper atmosphere would absorb the infra-red radiation from the Earth, thus increasing the greenhouse warming. This effect was found by Crutzen and his collaborators (see note 3, chapter 5) to be marginal, but was not included in earlier work. Washout by rain and snow could be significantly affected by the changed postnuclear climate, and the work of Covey et al. (see note 8, chapter 4) suggests that it would be reduced.

9 *Radiative transfer* The climatic changes result largely from the differing effect of smoke on the radition from the Sun and from the Earth. This 'radiative transfer' problem is not simple, but it is clear that the height of the smoke that absorbs most of the solar radiation is crucial. If this is higher than most of the atmospheric constituents that absorb and scatter infra-red radiation (say above about 5 kilometers), then there is an overall

cooling of the land, which is substantial if the smoke absorbs more than about half the sunlight. If not, then the effect is smaller, and in extreme circumstances there could possibly be a warming instead of a cooling.

10 *Height of smoke* Higher smoke produces more cooling. It also stays up longer. If it is in the postnuclear stratosphere, it may stay up for months or years rather than the week or two typical of the troposphere. The more powerful fires send their products higher, so they have an importance even greater than might be suggested by the proportion of the smoke that originates from them. Since they would be different from anything that has been observed, this is a major source of uncertainty.

11 *General atmospheric circulation* Computer models of more than one dimension are used to represent the horizontal motion of the atmosphere, which is an essential component of the climate. In these models the atmosphere is represented by its properties at points arranged as a mesh. The number of points determines the average size of the mesh. The smaller the mesh size, the better the model, but the greater the cost of running the computers. In practice this limitation is severe: for example, in the model of Covey et al. (note 8, chapter 4), the UK was represented by no more than one point. For other applications of the models it is possible to compensate partially for the effects of large mesh size by comparison with observation, and subsequent modification of the model, but this is of limited value for the postnuclear climate.

12 *Feedbacks* Where sunlight is substantially intercepted by smoke, the atmospheric circulation changes, and this change affects the subsequent movement of the smoke. The satisfactory treatment of this effect is just beginning. The extent of smoke transport across the

equator and of consequent Southern Hemisphere climatic changes is also still uncertain.

13 *Pollution* The extent of atmospheric pollution by the explosions and the fires, and then by the products of the subsequent chemical reactions in the atmosphere is very uncertain.

14 *Other effects* It is possible that the most important uncertainty has not been mentioned. Before Crutzen and Birks in 1982, no one had convincingly calculated the effect of smoke, which is now believed to be the major determinant of the postnuclear climate. Both the scientific knowledge and the need for this research have been present for at least twenty years. Even now the possibility that there is some other important but neglected effect cannot be ruled out, although this possibility becomes more remote as nuclear winter research expands and develops.

Mild and Severe Scenarios

One might think that with so many uncertainties, the research is of little value, but this is not so. Although it does not give certain predictions, it gives us the best available guide to the risks. One cannot predict with certainty that someone who smokes will get lung cancer, or that there will be an accident at some chemical plant causing the deaths of thousands of people, but one can make an estimate of the risks, and then try to reduce them. The global effects of nuclear war are different because it is not possible to check the unique aspects of the effects against observation: this makes the theoretical research all the more important.

The nuclear winter predictions follow from reasonably conservative assumptions, but the uncertainties imply that the present scenarios contain errors. These errors could go either way: the actual global effects could be more severe or less severe than those predicted at present. It is very unlikely that all the errors would conspire together to go in the same direction. Nevertheless, as uncertainties are reduced or removed, we should expect the predicted scenarios to change.

In addition to the uncertainties, variation can be caused by changes in the war scenario, or the season, or the weather before or during the main attacks of a nuclear war.

In order to provide some guide to the range of possible effects, we present four global effect scenarios. The first scenario is the baseline scenario described in chapter 2 to 4, whose consequences are followed throughout the rest of the book. This represents our estimate of the more likely global effects of a large-scale nuclear war, given the evidence at present available to us. Of three further scenarios whose effects are described below the first is a threshold scenario, in which the season and the physical assumptions are the same as for the baseline scenario, but the severity of the nuclear war is reduced to a level at which the expected global effects are no worse than for a major volcanic eruption. The other two are a relatively mild and a relatively severe scenario, that we believe are both consistent with present theories, and represent a rough guide to the range of possible uncertainty and variation. In these scenarious the war scenario is the same as for the baseline scenario, but the season and the weather differ, and differing assumptions are made about a few of the more important uncertainties. The discussion of the amount of smoke produced is based on the 1985 NRC Report (note 5, chapter 1).

Threshold Scenario

According to the results of TTAPS (note 2, chapter 1), a 1,000 megaton war, with similar targets to our baseline scenario, would produce about 8 times as much smoke and dust as would be necessary to produce a reduction in sunlight similar to that of the recent El Chichon volcanic eruption in Mexico. A 500 megaton war might, therefore, have a good chance of producing a similar climatic impact to one of the larger historical eruptions like Tambora in Indonesia in 1815. This is thought to have caused an average temperature drop of about 1°C in the Northern Hemisphere several months after the eruption. Yet 1816 was known as the year without summer: harvests failed over large areas and six inches of snow fell in New England, USA, in June.

The climatic effects depend on the targets: if the attacks were confined to missile silos and airfields far from cities, a 2,000 megaton war would produce the same effect as 500 megatons on all types of target, while 100 megatons might be enough to trigger a nuclear winter if it were concentrated on city centres. However, such special war scenarios are not likely to occur and so, on the rather limited evidence available, the threshold above which nuclear winter could occur should probably be taken as a war of between 500 and 1,000 megatons.

Mild Scenario

In this scenario the principal nuclear weapon exchange takes place in December, after a period of wet or snowy weather over most of the target areas.

Most of the forests are so wet or snow-covered that forest fires do not contribute significantly to the smoke. Neighbouring explosions over cities are sufficiently far apart in time that the smoke from fires significantly reduces the ignition area of the later explosions. Blast covers most of the combustible material in the high buildings of the central areas of the cities, so that relatively little of it burns. In suburbs, the fires do not get established so effectively, nor do they spread as much as in the baseline case. The total area burned is 50 per cent of the baseline value, and the amount of fuel burned is reduced by a half in the area that remains. The efficiency of smoke production is 50 per cent less also, reducing the amount of smoke to about 12 per cent of the baseline case described in the last chapter. With smaller fires, the plumes are not so high, and the smoke stays in the atmosphere for less than half the time of the baseline case.

The global effects of the war are dominated by the dust from the nucler explosions. Because much of the dust from the larger weapons goes into the stratosphere, the days are visibly dimmer than usual for many months, first in the Northern Hemisphere, and after 6 to 8 months in the Southern Hemisphere also, returning to normal after 2 or 3 years. There is twilight for many days or weeks for hundreds or thousands of miles downwind from the long-term fires that are likely in fuel stocks and cities.

Because the main nuclear exchange is in Winter the drop in temperature is about one third of that given by the "mild" graph of figure 4.4, with a maximum decrease of about 3°C in the Northern Hemisphere and 1° or 2°C in the Southern Hemisphere. This is still much worse than any recorded change due to volcanic eruptions, and would have a severe effect on agriculture.

However the lives lost from the global effects would probably be small compared to those dying from the direct effects of the war (see chapter 2). These already represent an unparalleled catastrophe. The mild scenario is only relatively mild.

Severe Scenario

The ignition area in towns and cities is increased by one-third over the baseline scenario and the blast explodes most of the buildings in such a way as to leave most of the combustible materials exposed. The proportion of material burned is one-quarter greater than baseline; the resulting firestorms are intense, burning the asphalt on most roads, producing particularly black smoke, and sending much non-combustible material along with the smoke up to the tropopause and beyond. The ignition of North American suburban houses with dry wooden roofs causes them to burn almost completely within an hour or so, and the fire winds lift flaming wooden tiles and other burning material into the air. In many cities the suburban smoke is drawn into firestorm plumes and reaches the tropopause. Oxygen depletion in large areas of the fires and rapid cooling in the plumes increase the amount of smoke produced, and washout in the plume is not great, so that the efficiency of smoke production is doubled. Overall the production of smoke is increased four times over the baseline value. In the regions covered by smoke clouds the warming of the smoke layer causes the tropopause to be depressed by 3 kilometers within a few days. So about 25 per cent of the smoke is found in the postnuclear stratosphere. The smoke in the postnuclear troposphere reaches the ground in a few weeks, leaving relatively clear air, with smoke slowly drifting in from above. The amount of smoke in the stratosphere in the severe case is roughly the same as the total amount of smoke in the baseline case. It rises during the day, when it is heated by the Sun, and mixes thoroughly with the air of the stratosphere up to a height at which the upward convection of smoke is balanced by the rate at which it falls by gravity.

This falling is much slower than for spherical dust particles, because the stratospheric smoke consists of sparse clusters of small smoke particles. The absorption of solar radiation by these clusters is little affected by their size, because it approximates that of the separated small particles. When it first reaches the stratosphere, the smoke reacts with the atmospheric ozone, but most of the smoke is saved from destruction by a layer formed from the great variety of materials swept up into the city fire plumes.

The heating of the stratosphere by the Sun produces an inversion layer between the smoke in the postnuclear stratosphere and the troosphere. The postnuclear troposphere is preserved by the heat of the oceans, but it decreases in height as the oceans slowly cool. The rate at which the stratospheric smoke would diffuse or mix into the troposphere and settle under these conditions is unknown; it could take many years. The smoke would certainly have time to spread over the whole globe. During the first few months the darkness and cold are significantly worse than in the baseline scenario. After this the sunlight reaching the ground is reduced on average to about 12 per cent of its normal value over the globe, and the sunlight then gradually increases.

In such a scenario the drop in temperature would be worldwide and catastrophic, going much lower than the minimum temperature for the baseline scenario for a period of a year or more. The drop could even happen after a winter war. In temperate climates it would be like a very severe winter or worse lasting for years. In tropical climates, it would be slightly warmer, but the contrast with normal conditions would be even greater. The oceans would have time to cool significantly, ensuring lower temperatures for many years. This severe scenario is worse than many others mainly because it takes into account the possibility of transfer of a large proportion of the smoke to the postnuclear stratosphere through the lowering of the tropopause.

The enormous contrast between the mild and the severe scenario demonstrates the great variation in the possible climatic consequences of a large scale thermonuclear war.

Summary

The study of the global atmospheric consequences of nuclear war contains many uncertainties, which may be reduced by further research, but cannot be eliminated. The uncertainties allow a wide range of possible global consequences of a large scale nuclear war, from a relatively mild scenario in which the lives lost as a result of the global effects would be small compared to those dying from the direct effects, to a severe scenario in which a nuclear winter lasts for a year or more over the globe. The research provides a useful assessment of the risks.

6 War on the Living

In this chapter we consider the effects of a nuclear winter on plants, animals and living systems. For living things the immediate effects of a nuclear war would be devastating — but they would not be global: most parts of the Southern Hemisphere and large areas in the Northern Hemisphere would escape blast, fires and short-term fallout. Nuclear winter, however, *would* affect the whole of the Northern Hemisphere and could well be global in its effects. Assuming that a nuclear war had occurred in May or early June involving about 6,000 megatons of explosive power (the scenario described in chapter 2), few places on Earth would escape entirely the long-term effects of reduced light and temperatures, global fallout and, eventually, increased UV–B radiation.

The multitude of problems that would afflict human populations — disease; economic, social and agricultural collapse; and, probably most serious of all, starvation — are discussed in detail in chapter 7. But these human problems cannot fully be understood without first examining the effects of a nuclear winter on other animals and plants. This is where the root of our predicament would lie because the most basic of all human needs is food and we depend on animals and plants to provide it.

Food supplies energy, which all living things need just to stay alive, let alone to grow. So if the flow of energy from the providers (plants) to the consumers (animals) is suddenly decreased, animals starve. Beefsteak comes from cows that eat grass; lions eat herbivores such as zebras that eat grass; and even sperm whales feed on krill that consume marine algal plants. All these food chains depend ultimately on growing plants and human food chains are no different. This is why the chapter begins by examining the effects of a nuclear winter on plant growth.

Plant survival can depend just as strongly on animals as the other way round. Plants need a fertile soil in order to grow, and soil animals, such as earthworms, play a vital role in maintaining fertility; seed must be set in order to produce a new generation, and many flowers depend on insects for pollination. The interactions are many, complex and delicate, easily upset by quite small changes in the environment and, therefore, very vulnerable to the massive disruption that nuclear war and nuclear winter would cause. Later in the chapter we try to assess what the effects of this disruption might be.

From existing knowledge one can be reasonably certain that the biological effects of a nuclear winter would be catastrophic. This does not mean that biologists have tested the effects of low light and freezing temperatures in the middle of summer, for who in their right mind would have done such experiments in the past? But there is enough information to make informed guesses about the effects of each stressful environmental change acting *in isolation*. What cannot be predicted with certainty is the *combined* effect of all these stresses acting together or in sequence. Plants, for example, are more easily damaged by ionizing radiation from fallout when temperature is low; and animals are usually more susceptible to cold if they are weak and starving. So from what little we know it seems likely that tolerance of one stress will be lower in the presence of other stresses. In other words, the effects of these various stresses may be interactive and not just additive.

Effects on Plants

The reason why green plants are the ultimate source of food is that they can obtain energy directly from sunlight. They manufacture their own food by the process called photosynthesis, in which light absorbed by green tissues is used to convert carbon-dioxide gas from the air into sugars, and oxygen is released as a by-product. Like animals, plants use energy constantly for simple maintenance and repair and this energy is obtained through respiration. Just as coal burns to release heat, so sugars 'burn' in a biologically controlled way during respiration.

For plants to grow, therefore, the energy trapped during daylight hours must exceed the energy used up in respiration throughout the 24 hours. It needs little imagination to see that if nuclear winter followed a late spring war, the chilly twilight conditions would greatly decrease photosynthesis and probably stop completely the production of plant food for the animal kingdom.

Light

Figure 6.1 shows how the amount of surplus or net photosynthesis (i.e. in excess of respiration) varies with light intensity for a patch of young grass. Net photosynthesis, and therefore growth and storage, is zero when light intensity falls to about 5–6 per cent of the noon value for a sunny June day — the light compensation point marked in figure 6.1. It could be darker than this for up to two weeks for our 6,000 megaton scenario and for up to two months for a more severe, 10,000 megaton scenario.[1]

So even if low light were the only problem, vegetation over much of the Northern Hemisphere would virtually stop growing and, in effect, starve for this period. Short-lived annual plants, which include all the major grain crops, would probably die. Trees and other perennials with greater food reserves might survive but they would be much weakened. They would be unlikely to form fruits or seeds, either because food reserves were too low or because the precise conditions of day length and temperature needed to flower were not met. Box 6.1 shows what happens to wheat plants when deprived of adequate light.

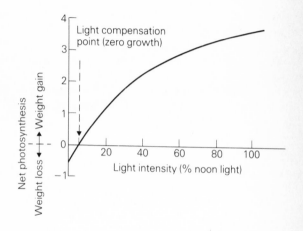

Figure 6.1. Photosynthesis and light[2]

Note: How net photosynthesis (measured as gain in dry weight/unit area/unit time) varied with light intensity for a sward of young grass in early June. The noon light intensity was for a cloudless, sunny day. Negative photosynthesis means a loss of dry weight.

Temperature

Low light would not, of course, be the only problem for plants during a nuclear winter. It would also be colder than usual with periods of freezing weather even in the middle of summer over large areas. Figure 6.2 shows how net photosynthesis of a Canadian grassland fell by over 70 per cent when the temperature dropped from 20 to 5°C.

Box 6.1

Cereal Crops and The Nuclear Winter: The Effect of Low Light on Wheat

Three-quarters of the world's staple food comes from wheat, maize and rice and the wheat yield is the largest of these three crops. The fate of many people in the Northern (and perhaps Southern) Hemisphere would depend critically on what happened to the wheat crop during a nuclear winter.

Wheat plants of three different ages were tested to find out what were the effects of various period of dim light. There was no decrease in temperature.

Conditions

Spring wheat (variety Regal Durum) was grown in large pots in a heated greenhouse with supplementary lighting. For periods of 1–6 weeks, pots were transferred to low light conditions that were about one per cent of the light level which saturates photosynthesis. Plants which survived this treatment were restored to normal light conditions in the greenhouse. The temperature was held at about 15°C throughout.

Results

Young stage (two-week-old plants) Dim light quickly stoped growth of the plants, which started to fall over after 1–2 weeks. A few survived as long as 6 weeks, probably living off reserves in the grain. They were however very small and pale and, although some recovered when restored to full light, the yield was small and greatly delayed.

Cereal crops and the nuclear winter

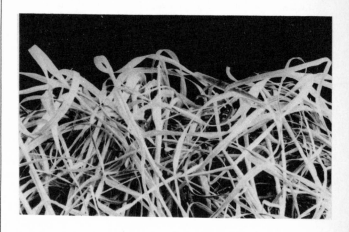

Plate 6.1. Spring wheat (variety Regal Durum) grown in a greenhouse until mature: a) under normal lighting conditions b) after transfer for two weeks to 1 per cent of normal light when six weeks old

Rapid growth stage (six-week-old plants) The effect of dim light was stronger at this stage, with growth checked and flowering delayed after only one week's treatment. Plants receiving 2 weeks of dim light went yellow and died back, but recovered when restored to full light by producing branches at ground level (tillers): the grain yield however was small and long delayed. All but one of the plants given 3 weeks of treatment did not survive, indicating how small the reserves of food may be in such highly bred cereal varieties. Plate 6.1b shows what these plants looked like.

Flowering stage (nine-week-old plants) By this stage the wheat plants had apparently built up more food reserves, and 2 weeks of dim light caused a relatively small check to growth. However, flowering and fruit set had been interrupted and the wheat ears did not contain any grain at all. Again there was a delayed yield from tillers, which amounted to only about one-quarter of that from plants receiving normal light throughout.

These tests were carried out by Alan Longman (Edinburgh) and were done primarily to prepare material for the BBC television programme *On the Eighth Day*. But they are sufficient to suggest that a nuclear war in spring or early summer might gravely deplete or eliminate yields throughout the north temperate cereal belt, simply through the temporary restriction of photosynthesis. More detailed experiments are urgently needed, to discover how various important crop and pasture plants might respond to combinations of reduced light, temperature drops, and other stress conditions predicted for a nuclear winter.

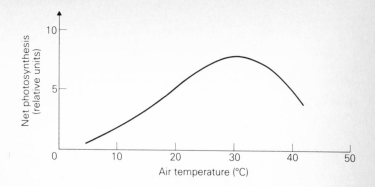

Figure 6.2. Photosynthesis and temperature[3]

Note: How net photosynthesis varied with air temperature for a Canadian mixed-grass prairie.

Similarly, it was calculated that a fall in average summer temperature of 1°C would reduce the yield of Canadian wheat by 46 per cent. So even a small change in average temperature could have marked effects on crop yields. In the temperate zone, where the UK, much of the US and the USSR lie, growth usually stops completely at around 5°C.

But quite apart from affecting photosynthesis, low temperatures can also damage plants. Appendix 6.1 describes the sorts of damage inflicted and what determines its severity. It should be clear from this that what might be lethal to many temperate plants would be the sharp fluctuations in temperature to below freezing — *in summer*. Tropical plants, on the other hand, can suffer lethal damage at temperatures well above freezing and at any time of year.

The Temperate Zone and Freezing Damage in Summer

Any gardener in the UK knows the dire effects of just one

night of air frost in late May or early June. Seedlings collapse, buds blacken and growth can be set back for the entire summer. Whole fruit crops can be lost, because flower buds and young fruits are particularly sensitive to frost.

Most damage is caused when ice crystals form inside cells and the range of temperatures at which this happens in summer are shown in table 6.1.

Every time a 'freezing episode' occurred during a nuclear winter, some and perhaps even all of the above-ground parts of plants might die — the severity of damage would depend on how cold it was and how long the cold lasted. Seedlings would almost certainly die because this stage of the life cycle is particularly susceptible to frost. Roots near the surface of the soil might also be killed unless there was an insulating blanket of snow:

Table 6.1 Cold limits for photosynthesis (PS) and the range of temperatures at which tissues freeze and die for various temperate zone plants in summer[4]

Species	Cold limit of PS/°C	Tissue-freezing temperature/°C
Conifers		
Scots pine (*Pinus sylvestris*)	−3.5	−3.0 to −4.4
Yew (*Taxus baccata*)	−4.9	−3.6 to −5.2
North European trees and shrubs		
Birch (*Betula pendula*)	−3.9	−3.2 to −4.1
Ivy (*Hedera helix*)	−3.0	−2.2 to −3.8
Bilberry (*Vaccinium myrtillus*)	−3.7	3.2 to −4.2
Mediterranean evergreen trees		
Lemon (*Citrus limon*)	−1.3	−3.2 to −4.2
Arctic or Alpine herbaceous plants		
Creeping avens (*Geum reptans*)	−3.0	−1.5 to −4.0
Mountain sorrel (*Oxyria digyna*)	—	−3.0 to −3.9

Note: °C–degrees centigrade.

−3°C is lethal to apple tree roots in summer and if the root system is badly damaged, a plant usually dies. Late spring frost has been known to kill entire oak trees in the Appalachian region of the US.

In coastal areas of the northern mid-latitudes, which include the UK, the warmth retained in the oceans is expected to make the temperature drops less severe. However, the strong winds predicted for these areas could be very damaging to plants, especially if rainfall were reduced and if the winds brought cold air from the continent. Another potentially severe problem in these areas could be alternations between relatively warm and freezing cold temperatures. This might be even more damaging than continuous cold because some plants might acquire a degree of cold resistance during cold spells (and use up scarce reserves of stored food to do so) but lose it rapidly during warmer spells (see appendix 6.1).

Taking into account the effects of low light and temperature on photosynthesis, frost damage and wide-spread pollution of air and soil, it is hard to avoid the conclusion that virtually no plants would grow in the UK or anywhere else in the north temperate zone. There would certainly be no harvest. Countless trees would be severely injured and many killed.

The Tropical Zone

Between the Equator and the Tropic of Cancer (23 degrees North) average surface temperatures on land are between 16 and 24°C in both January and July, so there is no real winter. This huge belt covers much of Africa, from the Congo and Kenya to the central Sahara and southern Egypt; most of the Indian sub-continent and the Far East from Borneo to just north of Hong Kong; and, in the Americas, stretches from Cuba to the Amazonian basin in central Brazil. The conditions predicted in our scenario for this zone are:

1 Low light occurring patchily two to three weeks after the attack and over most of the area within one to two months.

2 A fall in average temperature of, for example, 2–4°C in southern India and 3–7°C in Equatorial Africa, with occasional sharp temperature fluctuations of 5–10°C from these averages.

So the tropics might experience numerous short periods of a few days' duration when temperatures fell to below 10°C and perhaps even to below freezing.

This may not sound too bad but one has to remember that most tropical plant communities are adapted to conditions of high light and a warm, stable temperature regime. Growth and photosynthesis are inhibited much more by a fall in temperature than in the temperate zone. Many tropical plants cannot tolerate even a few hours of freezing temperature and none develops resistance to prolonged cold, whatever the time of year. Most important of all in the context of a nuclear winter, many tropical plants are damaged merely by chilling to below 10–15°C for a few days (see appendix 6.1). It is this chilling sensitivity coupled with conditions of low light intensity that could lead to zero growth and widespread plant death during a nuclear winter in the tropics.

Tropical crops would probably be severely affected and box 6.2 gives examples to illustrate this. Another point is that many important crop species grown in the temperate zone are of tropical origin — potatoes, tomatoes, cucumbers and maize, for example — and although the varieties used are more resistant to cold than the original tropical varieties, they still cannot withstand freezing of tissues and grow slowly, if at all, when severely chilled.

A nuclear winter in early summer would effectively wipe out the entire growing season in the temperate zone, severely reduce plant growth in the tropics and kill many species in both zones. Crop production throughout most of the Northern Hemisphere would stop.

Box 6.2

Chilling Damage to Tropical Plants and Crops by Tropical Origin

Species	Chilling treatment	Result	
Rice (*Oryza sativa*)	7°C during flower formation	Flowers do not form	Crop failure
Rice and hybrid sorghum[5]	13–16°C during pollen formation	Sterile pollen	
Cotton (*Gossypium arboreum*)	Exposure of seeds to 30 minutes at 12°C 2–4 hours after they start to absorb water	Seeds die or roots develop abnormally	
Maize (*Zea mays*) and Sorghum — some hybrid varieties (see note 4, chapter 6)	Chill to 10°C for 2.5 days and then restore to 25°C	Permanently inactivates photosynthesis in sorghum leaves and reduces the rate in maize to 33–67 per cent of that of controls (see figure 6.3)	Stops growth
Pasture legumes (similar to clovers) in Queensland, Australia.[6]	Grow plants at various temperatures down to the chilling range (see figure 6.4)	Severe growth inhibition by chilling, (note variety 1 in figure 6.4 — growth stopped when day temperatures were 24 and night temperatures 19°C)	

Further general effects of chilling to below 13 but above 0°C:

1 Chilling germinating seeds of soybean, lima bean, cucumber, peppers, tomato, aubergine and okra may cause damage ranging from complete crop failure to delayed maturity and reduced yields.
2 Chilling young plants can have delayed effects on leaf shape and size, plant height, root growth, flower formation and crop yield.
3 Chilling stored produce — yams, sweet potatoes, certain types of green bananas, citrus fruits, tomatoes, cucumbers, peppers, aubergines and peaches — can cause damage, reduce storage life and make some inedible.

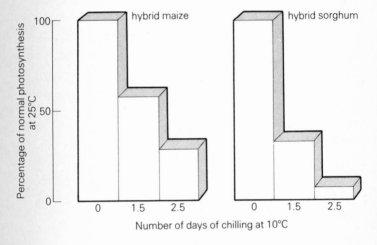

Figure 6.3. Photosynthesis after chilling stress[7]

Note: Hybrid maize and sorghum were grown at 25°C and then chilled at 10°C for 1.5 or 2.5 days. The histograms show photosynthesis (as percentage of the rate before chilling) of the youngest mature leaves 30 hours after the chilling period.

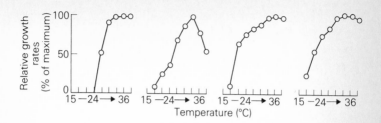

Figure 6.4. Effects of chilling temperatures on the growth of tropical legumes[8]

Note: Pasture legumes in Queensland, Australia, were grown at day temperatures ranging from 15 to 36°C, with night temperatures 5 lower in each case. The graphs show the relative growth rate of whole plants expressed as a percentage of the maximum rate recorded. Results for four varieties are shown: 1, Calopo; 2, Tinaroo glycine; 3, Green panic; 4, Guinea.

Surviving Plants

Ironically, the plants most likely to survive undamaged through the coldest and darkest months are humble lichens and mosses. Even tropical lichens can tolerate severe freezing and they have a remarkable ability to recover after rapid freezing and thawing. Surviving woody plants would be damaged and probably leafless, but with some buds still capable of sprouting: it would depend largely on how low temperatures had fallen (appendix 6.1). The plants killed to the ground, however, could survive in either or both of only two ways: as dry seeds, with a water content of less than 10 per cent, or as wet seeds, roots or storage organs that had been protected underground. This assumes that the soil did not freeze to a great depth during the nuclear winter or, in the temperate zone, the 'normal' winter that followed.

Single-celled or thread-like algae, which are the most important plants in lakes and the open sea, could have survived as spores. Provided that these had remained suspended in the water and had not sunk to a great depth, they would germinate when light levels returned to normal. On land, bacteria and fungi would also have survived mainly as spores but this is rather a mixed blessing. On the one hand, some of these micro-organisms are essential for maintaining soil fertility but, on the other, some cause serious disease in plants or animals. There are also a surprisingly large number of bacteria and fungi that grow actively at freezing tempera-tures (from about −5°C upwards), which is why food in a refrigerator rots or goes mouldy in time. This has serious implications for the preservation of stored food (chapter 7) but, in addition, the presence of pathogenic fungi and bacteria could pose a threat to regenerating plants: weakened or damaged plants would be much more likely to become infected.

Plant growth means *food*, so a key question affecting human and animal survival is about timing: when would plants start to regenerate after a nuclear winter and could the seedlings and young sprouts survive?

Suppose, for example, that new growth began to appear in the north temperate zone during late spring, about ten to twelve months after a nuclear attack. It could still be colder than usual (chapter 4); there would be universal, low-level radioactive pollution of soil and water from global fallout and some areas would be heavily polluted by early fallout or toxic chemicals; extensive soil erosion might have occurred wherever bare soil had been exposed. On top of all this, the amount of UV-B radiation could be approximately doubled. Each of these factors would tend to reduce plant growth, perhaps to only a small extent but, when the effects are added together, the overall reduction could be quite large.

In the tropics, regeneration might have started some-what earlier but conditions for plant growth would probably still be far from ideal. Potentially serious problems in both tropical and temperate zones could be alteration in the timing or amount of rainfall, and outbreaks of fungal disease and insect pests. These would affect natural vegetation but their effects on crop growth would be of greater concern from a human point of view. It is not unreasonable to assume that this growing season, the second affected by the nuclear war, would be a very poor one in both north temperate and tropical zones.

The only wild plants likely to grow relatively well and spread in post-war conditions would be weeds. By definition, these are opportunists: they often have wide tolerance of external conditions, they invade disturbed areas rapidly and many have enormous numbers of dormant seeds 'banked' in the soil. In modern agriculture weeds are controlled mainly by herbicides, but the absence of such control for post-war crops would mean that weeds became once again serious competitors with crops and crop yields would inevitably fall. Apart from weeds, trees and perennial plants are likely to regenerate only slowly after a nuclear war and, in Britain, a bleak landscape would be dominated by dead or dying trees.

Ultraviolet-B Radiation

As light levels returned to normal after a nuclear winter it seems fairly certain that increased amounts of damaging ultraviolet-B radiation would reach the Earth's surface (chapter 4). How serious the effects of this would be is still unclear and estimates range from 'insignificant'[9] to 'among the most serious unanticipated consequences of nuclear war'.[10] Box 6.3 describes what UV-B radiation is.

UV-B increases naturally with altitude and with decreasing latitude so that there is almost four times more at the equator than at the poles. But exposed alpine and equatorial plants have evolved natural defence mechanisms against UV-B damage and you cannot assume that lowland plants from temperate latitudes could endure the same conditions.

The kinds of damage caused to plants by UV-B include increased rates of mutation, reduced photosynthesis,

Box 6.3

What is UV-B?

Radiation from the sun has components of widely different wavelengths, ranging from invisible long-wave radiation (such as infra-red), through the wavelengths that can be seen as light, to invisible short-wave radiation — which includes ultraviolet (UV).

The position of UV-B in the solar spectrum is shown in figure 6.5, which shows that few of the shorter UV-B wavelengths reach the earth's surface because they are absorbed by the atmosphere (and especially by the ozone layer). It is these shorter wavelengths, however, that are most harmful to living organisms because they are absorbed strongly by cells and then damage, in particular, the genetic material, DNA, and the photosynthetic machinery of plants.[11] Even a small increase in these shorter wavelengths can do a great deal of biological damage. So, for example, a 16 per cent reduction in the thickness of the ozone layer causes an increase in UV-B radiation sufficient to cause 45–50 per cent more damage to DNA.

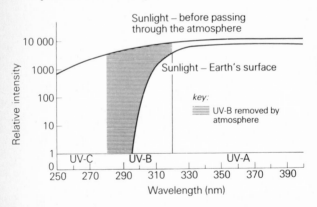

Figure 6.5. What is UV-B? Ultraviolet radiation with wavelengths between 280 and 315 nanometres (nm)

Note: The curves show the amounts of different UV wavelengths in sunlight (1) before it passes through the Earth's atmosphere; and (2) at the Earth's surface. After Caldwell, 'Plant responses to solar ultraviolet radiation' (see note 11, chapter 6).

production of smaller leaves and abnormal development, notably suppression of flowering and production of sterile pollen (see note 11, chapter 6). This last is potentially a very serious effect because it means that some plants (including crops) would be unable to set seed. In a recent experiment, pollen from four species of temperate plants was exposed for just 3 hours to UV-B levels about 3–4 times above normal: three species showed quite severe pollen damage.[12]

There is also concern about possible UV-B damage to phytoplankton — the minute algae that float near the surface of lakes and oceans and are at the base of aquatic food chains. These seem to be especially sensitive to UV-B, which can penetrate almost 40 meters through clear water and around 10 meters through more opaque water containing a lot of dissolved substances.

There is indeed uncertainty about the severity of UV-B damage. But bearing in mind that plant species vary greatly in their sensitivity to UV-B and that damaged or sickly plants are more susceptible, it would be foolish to assume that UV-B would cause few problems after a nuclear war. We know too little to be sure of this.

Summary of the Effects on Plants

Following the scenario set out in chapters 2 and 4 and assuming that a nuclear war had taken place in late May or early June causing atmospheric disturbances that led to a nuclear winter, then:

1. Growth and food storage by plants could be zero for up to 10 months in the north temperate zone and for up to 6 months in the tropical zone, due mainly to shortage of light and reduced temperatures.
2. Many plants in the Northern Hemisphere could die due to drops in temperature, incuding virtually all

temperate annuals and chilling-sensitive tropical species; all the major crop plants would be affected. Widespread damage to the above-ground parts of temperate and tropical perennials is also likely.

3. Regeneration of vegetation would be slow and patchy, with possible damage from UV-B, radioactive fallout and chemical pollution. Only weed species are likely to spread rapidly and they could become serious competitors of crop plants.

If, as predicted, the clouds of dust and smoke spread into the Southern Hemisphere, then the south tropical zone could suffer similar damage to the north. Damage in the south temperate zone, which includes parts of Australia, New Zealand, South Africa and South America, would be less. Partly this would be the result of smaller reductions in light and temperature but, in addition, it would be *winter* in this zone if nuclear war happened during the northern summer. Plants are much more resistant to cold during winter (see appendix 6.1).

Effects on Animals

We consider here only the direct effects of a summer war — cold and low light — on wild animals, leaving the major indirect effects — starvation due to lack of plant growth — until later in this chapter and the effects on domestic animals and humans until chapter 7.

Light

One effect of low light could be restriction of feeding by animals that depend on sight: some vertebrate predators, for example, and insects such as bees and butterflies. Nocturnal predators such as owls, with their specialized night vision, would be little affected, but day feeders like herons and hawks would have problems: imagine trying to spear fish in near darkness.

Other problems could arise because low light during a nuclear winter would effectively shorten day length for several weeks. It is common knowledge that swallows migrate south in autumn and wild animals mate and bear young at particular times of the year. So animals must 'know' what time of year it is and, in the temperate and polar zones, day length is one of the chief ways of knowing. The timing of nearly all the regular, seasonal activities of animals is influenced to some extent by day length and this timing could be disrupted by a nuclear winter. How serious this would be and how long before normal timing resumed is impossible to predict but species that migrate regularly and mammals and birds with strict seasonal breeding are likely to suffer most.

Temperature

More widespread than the effects of reduced light would be problems arising from low temperatures. These need to be considered for two groups, the 'cold-blooded' species, whose temperature varies with that of their surroundings and which include all the invertebrates (without backbones) and fish, amphibians and reptiles among vertebrates; and the warm-blooded species, which regulate their body temperature at a constant level and include all birds and mammals.

Low Temperature Effects on Cold-Blooded Animals

Just as growing plants suffer most from cold, so do cold-blooded animals that are breeding, feeding and generally active. This means that a spring or summer war would have the worst effects in the temperate zone and war at any time of year would have broadly similar effects in the tropics (except, perhaps for the areas with marked wet and dry seasons).

Cold-blooded animals would become increasingly torpid as temperatures fell. Development of young would be arrested, active movement and feeding would slow down and, since reserves of body fat are often minimal in summer, many animals could die — especially those living above ground.

Think of the situation for a hive of bees in (say) central Europe. There would be limited food stocks in the hive; many developing young and eggs; and low light and adverse temperature and wind conditions would probably make it impossible to forage for what little nectar and pollen were available. Most worker bees would die and the species could survive only if some queen bees remained alive — which would be possible but by no means certain.

Virtually no insects would be able to carry on flying, so insect-pollinated flowers, even if they survived, would be unable to set seed or form fruits. For large species such as dragonflies, for example, the minimum body temperature necessary for flight is usually 19–22°C: if air temperatures are below this then basking in the sun or whirring the wings to generate heat internally are carried out as warm-up devices. There would be no sun to bask in during a nuclear winter and stores of body fat for generating heat internally would soon be used up. In addition, flying insects are easily killed by wind-blown dust, and there could be a great deal of this in target countries.

The damage would be worse if temperatures fell to below freezing because few of these animals can survive freezing in summer. Even those species that usually survive cold winters in the temperate zone might be unable to do so during a nuclear winter in summer, since their bodies might be 'unprepared'. They might either be lacking adequate food stores, or be at the wrong stage of their life cycle — insect eggs or pupae can often survive low temperatures that are lethal to adults.

Cold-blooded animals in the tropics are generally less

tolerant of low temperatures than those at higher latitudes. Some tropical lizards die from chronic exposure at only 16°C; and many freshwater tropical fish are notoriously sensitive to cold. Species of the African fish, *Tilapia*, may die if water temperate falls below about 20°C, for instance, and this group includes the major food fish raised in fish ponds or caught in the African tropical lakes. Their situation is similar to that of chilling-sensitive tropical plants and the inference is the same: even quite small decreases in temperature in the tropical zone could be lethal for many cold-blooded animals.

Survival of these animals would, therefore, depend on three main factors:

1. Could they survive cooling by at least 5–10 degrees centigrade? Clearly some tropical species could not but many temperate species could.

2. Could they find shelter, perhaps underground or under snow cover, and avoid predation and, above all, freezing?

3. Having found shelter and/or become torpid, would their bodies contain sufficient stored food to last for perhaps months without feeding? A common cause of winter mortality in some reptiles and amphibians seems to be starvation of younger animals, which have lower fat deposits.

There would be survivors, however, particularly among the hordes of animals that live below ground. These include pests such as leather jackets (the larvae of crane-flies) and many useful animals, such as earthworms, that feed on dead plant remains and organic matter in the soil. Provided the soil did not freeze too deeply, these animals would be relatively unharmed and, moreover, there would be no shortage of food for those able to feed. Death rates would be much higher for above-ground species but some individuals, particularly among insects and particularly in the temperate zone, would probably persist as eggs, pupae or even adults in sheltered spots. Insects such as cockroaches and silverfish that cohabit with humans might survive in quite large numbers. Even if very small numbers of insects survived, however, an important point is that some species have tremendous powers of reproduction, especially those, such as aphids, that we look on as pests. Provided that food were available, numbers in these species would soon increase once the climate warmed up, and an obvious source of food would be newly-planted crops.

Low Temperature Effects on Warm-Blooded Animals

These species might be expected to fare better because of their built-in heating systems. But, for a summer war and in conditions of limited food supply, the opposite is likely to be true. Warm-blooded animals do not have the option of becoming torpid if outside temperatures fall, and most die if body temperature drops by only 3–5°C.

Maintaining a high body temperature uses up a lot of energy and, since insulation by fur or feathers is minimal in summer and body fat is depleted during the breeding season, these animals could survive a summer war only if they managed to find sufficient food. The young, weak and old and specialized feeders such as insect-eating swifts, swallows and bats would be very unlikely to do so.

For mammals and birds in the temperate and polar zones, the problem with a nuclear winter in summer would be that few of the usual ways of surviving cold winters would be feasible. Migration to warmer places (if there were any) would be impossible without the proper timing cues and without adequate stores of body fat. Heat loss could not be reduced by depositing layers of insulating fat or growing thicker fur or more feathers because there would not be sufficient time. Birds breeding in the arctic tundra might even be caught actually moulting their feathers. And the only remaining option, increasing the rate of internal heat production, uses up existing stores of body fat, requires a very high food intake to sustain it and, on its own, is not very effective against severe cold.

Most vulnerable would be the smallest mammals and birds, whose bodies have a high ratio of surface to volume and lose heat very easily. These would probably suffer very high death rates with extinction of some species. In the tropics, hummingbirds may die if average air temperatures drop by as little as 5°C; and even during a moderately severe British winter, 30 per cent of field mice have been reported as dying each winter month, presumably from cold and lack of food. The only exceptions would be animals such as mice and rats that are closely associated with humans and could take advantage of our shelter and food supplies.

One other major factor would affect survival of warm-blooded species in the temperate zone. Even if they survived a nuclear winter in summer, they must then face a 'normal' winter. This always involves lengthy and elaborate preparations, some of which we mentioned earlier: building up stores of body fat; preparing caches of food; and developing thick fur or feathers, for example. But none of these preparations would have been possible during the nuclear winter and there is a strong possibility that very few animals would survive until spring; most would die of cold and starvation.

Even for animals that survived all these hazards, there could still be problems caused by pollution, global fallout and increased levels of UV-B. Radioactivity could accumulate along food chains to reach dangerous levels in carnivores, including human beings, and this is considered in more detail later. UV-B may damage the cornea of the eye, causing blindness, and seems to suppress the immune system in mammals, increasing their susceptibility to disease.

Summary of Effects on Animals

Following a summer war, the populations of nearly all terrestrial animals that lived above ground would be greatly reduced. Cold-blooded animals, especially insects and species that live and feed in the soil, would be more likely to survive than warm-blooded animals. Bees, one of the most important pollinating insects, could be severely affected but insects with the ability to reproduce rapidly might recover quite swiftly.

Ultimately, species survival would depend on whether or not individuals lasted out until conditions suitable for breeding returned. Among mammals and birds survival would be quite probable for a few highly adaptable types of mammals, such as mice and rats, but very uncertain for most wild species: there would be widespread extinctions (especially among small mammals and birds in the north temperate zone) and populations would be reduced everywhere. Overall, a very unablanced and impoverished fauna seems the most likely outcome.

These and the effects described earlier for plants relate only to a nuclear war in early summer. Before we consider the wider ecological effects of a summer war we need to discuss briefly what would happen to animals and plants if a nuclear war occurred in winter.

Winter War

A nuclear winter superimposed on a normal winter in the temperate zone would result in exceptionally severe weather but the *relative* effect would be less severe than for a summer war. The reason is simply that light intensity and temperature are low in any case during winter. It would be a different story in the tropics, however, where summer/winter seasonality decreases progressively towards the equator: the biological effects of a nuclear winter here would be much the same whatever the time of year.

Further north, plants and animals would be fully prepared for winter conditions and much less damage would be inflicted by semi-darkness and arctic temperatures. Summer migrants, such as swallows, would have departed — although possibly to die in the tropics. Many invertebrate animals and non-woody plants would be in a cold-resistant resting stage — as eggs, pupae, seeds or roots, for example. Trees and shrubs would be fully cold-hardened and warm-blooded vertebrates either hibernating or prepared for activity in very cold conditions.

Figure 6.6 shows how effective cold hardening is in sycamore and how sharp the contrast between winter and summer. This is why plants can survive temperatures of −40 or −50°C in places such as Greenland, Siberia or northern Canada.

But anyone who remembers the exceptionally severe British winters of 1948, 1962–3 and 1981–2 will probably appreciate that, even in a relatively mild climate, *long* periods below freezing cause many deaths among birds and smaller mammals. The single night in January 1982 when temperatures fell below −20°C in parts of Britain caused devastation among garden trees and shrubs and even damaged some native species. So very severe winters do kill or damage even cold-hardened plants and well-prepared animals.

Possibly the most severe effects of a nuclear winter that started in winter, would arise from the long delay before the *next* growing season. New leaves might not appear until mid-summer and many plants might be unable to complete their cycle of flowering and seed set. So there would be a great shortage of food for animals and a disastrous growing season for agricultural crops.[13] It is possible, moreover, that insects could have survived the previous terrible winter more successfully than plants and might then become serious pests as plants struggled to grow.

The north temperate zone would certainly not escape unscathed if nuclear war occurred in winter. The tropics would be almost as badly affected as by a summer war

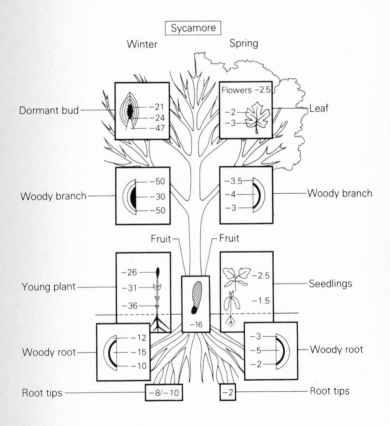

Figure 6.6. Frost resistance in different tissues of Sycamore (*Acer pseudoplatanus*) in winter and during sprouting in spring

Note: a) Numbers are the temperatures (°C) at which death or severe injury occurs.

b) Based on Larcher and Bauer, 'Ecological significance of resistance to low temperature' (see note 5, chapter 6).

and, furthermore, damage in the temperate zone of the Southern Hemisphere might even be worse. It would be summer in this region, so that plants and animals would be at their most vulnerable.

Effects on Ecosystems

We have considered separately the immediate effects of a nuclear winter on plants and animals; but of course they do not live in isolation from each other but as closely integrated communities. A full assessment of biological damage is possible only by considering possible effects on higher levels of organization — on ecosystems. At the simplest level, an ecosystem is all the living things in a given area together with their non-living environment. So it might be a wood, a lake, the East African savannah or the Amazonian rainforest. The important things to know about an ecosystem are: how it functions — how much energy and materials come in and go out; what maintains it in a particular state; and what sorts of changes could destabilize the system. You might ask similar questions of a human system such as a city or a country.

The functioning and survival of an ecosystem depends on innumerable interactions between its components — animals, plants, soil or water, and climate. Perhaps the most devastating and long-lasting effects of a nuclear winter could be on these interactions and we shall consider here some of the problems that might arise for terrestrial and aquatic ecosystems — leaving agricultural ecosystems, on which human survival will ultimately depend, until chapter 7.

Energy Problems

Every living thing in an ecosystem needs energy — light for plants and 'food' (more accurately 'organic matter') for other creatures. If the flow of energy into an ecosystem, out of it or between its different compartments alters radically, then the whole system will change, often with far-reaching results. A nuclear winter would reduce energy inputs by decreasing the amount of plant photosynthesis and this would mean less energy passing along the grazing food chain, which depends on living plants — and feeds human beings.

Terrestrial Ecosystems

If there were a summer war followed by months of almost zero plant growth and storage, then even the herbivores that survived the cold would begin to run short of food. Some might eat dead plants — but not all could because this requires specialized digestive systems. Others might survive on residual live tissues — seeds, bark or buds, for example. But the supply of these is limited and eating bark is particularly damaging to trees: dead trees are quite a common sight after severe winters, when sheep or deer have removed a complete ring of bark. As herbivore populations declined, it would become increasingly difficult for specialized carnivores to find food and the grazing food chains would begin to collapse.

Scavengers, however, would probably do rather well in the short term and one other part of terrestrial ecosystems would have an adequate supply of food — the soil system. Food chains in the soil are based mainly on dead plant remains and comprise worms, insects and countless other small animals, plus the bacteria and fungi that finally rot away the material. Human beings scarcely tap these decomposer food chains at all, agriculture being based firmly on the grazing food chains, so temporary abundance here would be of little use to starving human populations. Moreover if the whole ecosystem 'ran down', with plants taking many years to recover, then even the decomposers might be affected.

Major dislocation of the energy relationships of terrestrial ecosystems basically spells starvation for most animals, probably with damaging consequences for plants. Freshwater ecosystems — streams, rivers and lakes — would be similarly affected: after a summer war they would suffer widespread damage to plants and animals from cold, lack of light and pollution (which is discussed later). Things might be different in the oceans, however.

Marine Ecosystems

During a nuclear winter the surface waters of the oceans would stay comparatively warm — at least compared with the land. In northern waters a slow fall of only 3–4°C is predicted (chapter 4). So apart from ecosystems such as coral reefs, which are very sensitive to temperature, life elsewhere might be expected to carry on much as usual.

In fact it would not, because the reduction in light would disrupt energy flow in marine ecosystems just as badly as on land. The single-celled algae (phytoplankton) at the base of marine food chains would be unable to grow and multiply for several weeks in the twilight conditions. But these plants have life cycles usually measured in days, so they would either die or enter a dormant, resting stage (and it is not certain that this last option is possible in summer).

The small animals (zooplankton) that feed on phytoplankton would rapidly go short of food in summer, although in winter, when those in the temperate zone have large stores of fats, they might survive for weeks or even months. If zooplankton numbers fell then so, in turn, would the stocks of fish that feed on them. This collapse of grazing food chains would be slower and less dramatic than on land but the end result might be just as severe.

Since fish are an important source of food for human populations and might be even more so in the aftermath of a nuclear war, this prediction for marine ecosystems has important implications for human survival. In this context, another relevant point is that the richest fishing grounds are mostly in coastal waters and continental shelf areas (such as the North Sea) and these ecosystems could become severely polluted by chemicals and radioactive fallout washed in via rivers. So even if boats and fuel were available and skilled fishermen willing to brave the storms predicted around norther coasts, there might be few fish to catch and they might be unsafe to eat.

Other Interactions

Apart from food chains there are many other essential links between animals and plants — pollination, for example. Bees would starve if there were no flowers to provide pollen and nectar. So would the adults of other pollinators such as butterflies, small beetles and flies — and they would almost certainly be unable to lay eggs. If populations of these insects declined (and most do not have such powers of rapid reproduction as aphids and blowflies), then the first effect felt by human survivors would be a shortage of fruit and some vegetables. Nearly all the cultivated apples and plums, not to mention numerous wild fruits, require cross pollination by insects; beehives are commonly placed in orchards at a density of about one to the acre. In the extreme case that pollinating insects became extinct over large areas, insect-pollinated plants would be unable to set seed and they too might become extinct in the longer term.

Plant-pollinator relationships can be wonderfully intricate, with flowers having precise adaptations that allow pollination by just one species of insect, which in turn is totally dependent on that plant for survival. There are numerous similar examples where species are interdependent and extinction for one spells disaster for the other. In the first report of the biological effects of nuclear winter 'cascades of extinctions' were predicted extending over many years,[14] and all the available evidence seems to support this conclusion.

Water, Soil and Climate

Plants, soils, water and climate interact in a variety of ways that could be disrupted by the effects of a nuclear war and a nuclear winter. One example is described here.

When plant cover is destroyed over large areas, particularly forests, then the movement of water through the ecosystem and even the pattern of rainfall can be quite severely disturbed. Plants take up water from the soil constantly through their roots, lose it to the atmosphere by evaporation from leaves (mainly during the day) and hold an enormous reservoir of water in their tissues. In effect, the vegetation acts like a giant sponge; if it is killed or removed, the soil alone has only the absorptive qualities of a face flannel. The bare soil holds less water and rain percolates through less easily than when vegetation is present. So there is an increase in surface run-off, which erodes away fertile topsoil, puts a large extra burden of silt into rivers and may cause them to flood. Furthermore, the reduced amount of evaporation into the atmosphere may, in some conditions, reduce cloud formation and rainfall may decrease in areas downwind.

Such changes are occurring already in many parts of the world following large-scale deforestation or over-grazing, and they could be a very serious long-term problem in the aftermath of nuclear war. Disturbed areas without plant cover are also likely to suffer from soil erosion by wind or water. Since most of the radioactive fallout would be in the top layer of soil, one effect of erosion would be to concentrate fallout in rivers, creating problems for human water supplies and increasing the pollution of coastal waters.

Pollution

Pollution is certain to be a long term problem after nuclear war and the problems we have now pale into insignificance by comparison. Nearly all factories contain stores of toxic chemicals, and some have very large quantities indeed. These could be released in target areas. As cities burned, producing pyrotoxins from plastics, and as volatile liquids escaped from factories, acute pollution of the atmosphere would be the first effect. The death of over 2,500 people in Bhopal, India, late in 1984 is a grim parallel, and this was the result of an accidental release of toxic gas from just one factory.

When toxic liquids drained away and dry toxins dispersed as dust, wider pollution of the soil and water could occur. There would also be global pollution by radioactive fallout.

The long term ecosystem effects of this pollution would depend on the persistence of the chemicals and radio-isotopes. Some chemicals are broken down quite quickly but others — for example compounds containing heavy metals such as mercury and lead — are stable and might be absorbed by plants and animals. Some radio-isotopes decay within days into harmless isotopes (they are said to have a short half-life); but others have long half-lives and the most dangerous are also easily absorbed by living organisms. Strontium-90 and caesium-137 are two such isotopes.

Organisms differ greatly in their sensitivity to chemical and radioactive pollutants, with plants and insects being generally more resistant than mammals (including humans, who are very sensitive). Among plants, conifer trees are among the most sensitive with deciduous trees, shrubs, herbs, mosses and lichens following in order of increasing resistance. It seems, therefore, that forests and especially conifer forests would suffer the worst damage from pollution, and that grassland ecosystems would be among the least affected.

The most serious danger to animals occurs when toxins are concentrated along food chains in ecosystems. Thus plants can accumulate higher levels than the soil, herbi-vores higher levels than plants and carnivores the highest levels of all. This was why DDT caused so much damage to carnivorous birds such as hawks; and why offshore pollution with mercuric compounds has caused deaths among local people who ate much locally caught fish. The damage is compounded if toxins accumulate in particular organs; strontium-90, for example, concentrates in bone.

Such food chain effects are likely to be most serious in terrestrial ecosystems and in chapter 7 we describe an example where humans are the top consumers. For aquatic ecosystems, the available evidence suggests that effects would not be very serious in the open ocean but might be for lakes and reefs or shallow, coastal ecosystems. We mentioned earlier that coasts could be severely polluted by silt-laden, contaminated rivers: filter-feeding animals such as shrimps and mussels could accumulate high levels of toxins here and would not be safe for human consumption.

Succession and Recovery

Could ecosystems recover from the effects of a nuclear war and a nuclear winter? Probably most *would* recover in some form, but the questions then are how long would it take and what would they be like?

By considering just *one* stress at a time and making several simplifying assumptions, it has been possible to predict what might happen to a forest and to a grassland ecosystem. Mark Harwell describes the results of this computer simulation exercise in detail in his book *The human and environmental consequences of nuclear war* (note 10, chapter 6) and a summary of some results is given in appendix 6.2. For this exercise the reductions in temperature and light are much smaller than those predicted during a nuclear winter but they also continue for longer. So these calculations are not intended to simulate a nuclear winter but they do give some idea of how long ecosystems take to recover from milder but more prolonged stress. Forests take decades to recover from even the smallest drop in temperature whilst grassland recovers in a few years.

However, there is no computer programme in existence that can simulate the effects on ecosystems of the *combined* effects of a nuclear war; reduced light and temperature; radioactive fallout; increased UV-B radiation; pollution; and selective extinctions. It would certainly be the most devastating global disturbance since the human species evolved.

When terrestrial ecosystems are violently disturbed by events such as earthquakes, which leave large areas of bare ground, the recovery process follows the normal process of plant succession. Opportunist, weedy species first invade the bare patches; then shrubs and (if the climate is wet enough) trees, grow up from seeds buried in the ground or carried in by wind or animals. So herbaceous vegetation is succeeded by scrub and eventually by forest. It is a slow process that may, even in ideal conditions, take 20 years for wet, tropical forests, 50–100 years for lowland, temperate forest and 200 years for an upland oakwood in southern England.

Almost certainly, succession would be a great deal slower after a nuclear war. Adaptable pioneer species would probably form a cover of green plants despite the poor conditions for plant growth. But beyond this stage, the availability of seeds could become a major factor limiting succession. Most trees, for example, do not have large numbers of seeds lying dormant in the soil — they produce fresh seeds at regular intervals and these remain viable for a relatively short time. So if trees were destroyed over large areas, there is a risk that they might not become re-established for many years and perhaps not at all. Unless residual seeds managed to germinate and establish within one or two years of a war, when conditions would be very hostile, the species would either become extinct or spread back very slowly from undamaged plants many miles away. In the early post-war years there could be few insect pollinators or animals to carry seeds (one of the chief means of dispersal). Population explosions among insect pests, unregulated by the usual factors, could slow things down even further.

The conclusion is inescapable that natural ecosystems would take many years to recover: for forests, it would be many decades. Where numerous species had become extinct, terrestrial ecosystems might never return to their original state. The truth is, we do not know what the natural world would be like 10 or even 100 years after a nuclear war but it would be a changed and much poorer world.

7 The Human Cost

How would the long-term environmental effects of nuclear war affect human beings who had escaped blast, fires and radiation sickness? In terms of human death and suffering they could be more serious than the immediate effects and they would certainly be more widespread, with grave implications for people in every country of the world. This chapter explains the sorts of problems that human populations might have to face and why the effects are so serious and far-reaching.

What Condition Would We be In?

Whether or not individuals, groups or whole societies can survive periods of great stress depends strongly on their initial state — their physical and mental well-being. Human beings resemble plants and animals in some respects, such as having a lower resistance to cold, disease, or ionizing radiation when they are weak or injured (chapter 6). So we need to consider briefly the condition of people and their technological support systems at the beginning of a nuclear winter.

Inside Target Areas

In heavily targeted areas such as Europe, the USA and

USSR, most civilian survivors would probably be in a state of deep shock and terrible confusion. Eight out of ten of the UK population and five to eight out of ten in the USA could be dead or seriously injured (which probably means dead in the absence of medical care).

Supplies of gas, electricity, fuel and water would be disrupted; normal systems of transport and communication (radio, television and telephone) would be out of action; and the emergency and medical services would be in a state of chaos. In these circumstances, it is quite possible that people would become psychologically numbed, completely withdrawn and apathetic, and they would be in the worst possible state to face the additional rigours of a nuclear winter.

Outside Target Areas

For countries that were not targeted by nuclear bombs, fear, confusion and possibly civil disorder would spread as they lost contact with the target countries. These would increase as the effects of a nuclear winter were felt and, within weeks, people would begin to suffer because of the cessation of trade. Imports of food and energy (mostly oil) sustain many of these countries and, with few exceptions, derive from the target areas. Even food exporting countries such as Australia and New Zealand are almost totally dependent on energy imports. Third World countries in Africa, Asia and parts of South America depend heavily on food imports from Europe or North America and, even if their own agriculture were undamaged, their people would face severe food shortages after a nuclear war.

In the longer term, world-wide food shortages together with serious health problems could be the greatest threat. They are the main reason why more people might die of starvation and disease than in the war itself and most of this chapter is about these problems.

First, however, we consider the early effects of a nuclear winter and particularly the effects of cold on people in the north temperate zone.

Cold and the Early Effects of a Nuclear Winter

Old people die every year from hypothermia because they cannot keep warm, even in their own homes. Occasionally, fit young people who get lost while out walking die from exposure, because they become chilled or soaked to the skin and cannot maintain their body temperature. So, whether described as hypothermia or exposure, death from the effects of cold is not uncommon in civilized societies, even under quite mild temperature conditions. The question we must ask is to what extent human death from cold is a likely outcome of a nuclear winter.

Cold threatens human life whenever the rate at which heat is produced by the body (through metabolism and muscular activity) falls below the rate at which heat is lost from the surface. The real danger is when the deep tissue or 'core' temperature begins to drop below 37°C; people lose consciousness when the core temperature falls to 30°C, and by 27°C the heart stops beating.

If a normal, healthy human being starts to 'feel cold', there may be a voluntary, behavioural response — putting on more clothes, moving about or seeking shelter; but the involuntary reponse, in which the body burns up more fuel and increases the rate of heat production, is probably more important. When people are in a state of shock or have low reserves of body fuels and no food available for immediate consumption, it is the breakdown of both voluntary and involuntary temperature regulation that causes hypothermia. These conditions would be all too likely during a nuclear winter. So in the temperate zone, a fall in temperature even from the summer to winter average, and not necessarily far below freezing, might be lethal to weakened individuals. Babies and small children would be particularly at risk because their small bodies lose heat very easily.

For stronger, better-nourished individuals, the risk would be small provided that they continued to eat regularly and tried actively to keep warm: found shelter, built fires and put on sufficient dry clothing. This would not be easy. Fuel supplies would be cut off and, in the target zone, windows broken over large areas. Many modern houses do not even have a fireplace for burning wood. How many ordinary people could survive a winter in unheated houses with little food?

Even in coastal regions, where it would be less cold, areas such as the UK and California could experience severe gales and windchill could be an important factor. The cooling power of air increases strikingly as wind speed rises. For example, air at 0°C can cool exposed skin to about +19°C in still air but cools it to −18°C in a 40 miles-per-hour wind. During a nuclear winter, therefore, an appreciable number of people would probably die from the direct effects of low temperature — especially in the north temperature zone.

If it became sufficiently cold to freeze surface water, then this would compound another problem: how to obtain water. For city dwellers and for most people in developed countries, water is something that is taken for granted: it comes out of a tap and it flushes away sewage. We rarely think of the complex technology that supports the system on which life and health depend. After a nuclear war, that system would be destroyed beyond repair in many parts of Europe and North America and, without power to pump water from reservoirs or under-ground sources, many people would have to depend on wells accessible by hand power or on local streams, rivers and lakes.

But using surface waters could be dangerous or difficult. Within the target areas many water bodies would be contaminated by fallout or chemical pollutants and people could never be *certain* that they were safe. Collecting rain or snow would almost certainly be unsafe because it would be laden with radioactive dust and, often, toxic chemicals from fires and explosions. Away from the warmer coastal regions, it might even be cold enough to freeze surface water to a considerable depth and much energy would be needed to break ice and melt it. Getting enough water for drinking, let alone sanitation, could be quite a problem during a nuclear winter and people would most likely use any water that was available — even if it *were* dangerously polluted. This would cause further deaths.

Provided that water could be obtained, however, the problem that would rapidly dominate all others during a nuclear winter would be *food*. How long would stocks last, how could we get more, and when would agriculture recover? Prospects for human survival depend critically on the answers to these questions.

The Problem of Food Supply

Food Stocks

An average, urban family in the developed countries keeps very little food in reserve. Some families in Western Europe and the USA buy food on a daily basis, although most households probably have sufficient food to last for a week, perhaps even a month on a restricted diet. Most local supermarkets also carry little stock: even dry and tinned foods are usually replenished weekly from centralized depots, nearly all of which are in large towns or cities. Both cities and transport systems would be largely destroyed after a nuclear war, so without new deliveries, food stocks in an average town would fall to zero within two to four weeks — even without hoarding or looting.

People would then be dependent on widely dispersed government food stocks.

Most Western nations have emergency food stores and in the UK, for example, there are about 100 such buffer depots scattered around the country. If these had not been destroyed (and some undoubtedly would have been) and if the food could be distributed, they could probably feed survivors for a few weeks. So after a nuclear war in early June, people in developed Western countries would have used up most of the stocks of processed food by about September. There would have been no harvest and farms would, therefore, hold little stored food. The only remaining stocks would be of surplus agricultural produce held in government or EEC-controlled stores. Apart from butter and cheese, most of this produce is unprocessed cereals and pulses (soyabeans in the US, for example).

The more sophisticated a society is, the more complex and energy-dependent are the systems for storing, processing and distributing food and the more vulnerable these are to dislocation following a nuclear war.

Consider first the situation in Western Europe. The EEC controls hundreds of 'intervention' stores for grain, butter and other produce; there are about 140 grain stores in Britain alone and a total of 10 million tonnes of surplus dairy produce throughout Europe. Most of these stores are in rural areas close to the sites of production, so perhaps half might survive a nuclear war and that should be sufficient to feed the remaining population for at least a year.

For the USA, David Pimentel has calculated that if there were no food exports and a drastic reduction in the amount of grain fed to livestock (currently around 40 per cent of the annual harvest), then about 200 million tonnes of grain and protein-rich beans would be available for human consumption — enough to keep the *present* US population eating as vegetarians for nearly three years.[1] In theory, therefore, Western Europe and North America could feed their human populations, and even some livestock, right through a nuclear winter and for a considerable time after.

Theory and reality could well be very different, however. Firstly, large food stores need careful management if the food is not to rot and spoil. Stored grain requires precise control of humidity; it must be regularly turned over by large machines; and rodents and insect pests must be rigorously excluded. This level of care would be difficult and probably impossible after a nuclear war, so large amounts of food might be wasted.

A second problem would be processing this 'raw' food. Western city dwellers have neither the skill nor equipment to grind grain and, without power, modern processing plants would be useless. No doubt individual solutions to this difficulty would be found but for ill and weakened survivors, it would be one more burden to bear.

The third and probably most difficult problem would be distribution. With transport systems in ruins, how could food be carried from stores in rural areas to the survivors in cities? The inadequacy or absence of plans for food distribution in the UK after a nuclear war are described graphically in Duncan Campbell's book on Civil Defence, *War plan UK*.[2] Writing before the possibility of a nuclear winter was widely known, his estimate of the likely effects of a war in early summer were that 'the next winter would see many millions starve, unless the number of survivors was already tiny'.[3] Stored food might simply be inaccessible to the majority of survivors.

This is the situation for countries well provided with food. But some nations, although technologically advanced, do not have large food stocks. The USSR, China and India fall into this category. These countries import grain and without either imports or home production, their grain stocks would soon be exhausted. The USSR and China have food stocks sufficient to maintain their present populations for about 4 months; India would run out of food in one month (or two months on starvation rations). Unless a high proportion of the population were killed in the early days of a nuclear war, the people of these countries would face mass starvation before the next harvest. Their only choice is between a quick death and a slow one.

Food in the Developing Countries

Starvation or bare subsistence is already the fate of millions in Third World countries. Whilst North America and Europe harvest enough food in peacetime to feed the entire world, South America and Asia produce sufficient barely to meet their needs, and Africa produces only half the food it needs. Many developing countries therefore depend heavily on food imports or, in emergencies, food aid. Ethiopia alone, after three years of drought, requires 100,000 tonnes of grain each month just to keep people alive. For countries in such a desperate situation, the main effect of a nuclear war would be mass starvation within weeks as the flow of aid stopped.

In developing countries where there was no famine, the immediate impact of a nuclear war on food supplies would vary between rural and urban populations. Rural families may hold supplies of some basic foods sufficient to meet their needs at least between one harvest and the next; the more seasonal the climate, the more common this practice. But urban populations rarely hold food stocks and often depend heavily on imported food. Since a nuclear winter would destroy or greatly reduce the next harvest (chapter 6), the food situation in these countries would depend at first on three factors:

1 Their level of dependence on imported food, with urban populations likely to suffer the worst shortages.
2 The time of year when the war happened relative to the main harvest, which would affect both urban and (especially) rural populations. Just before the harvest would be the worst time.

3 The amount and keeping qualities of any food stocks held, which would also affect most of the population.

Production of some major tropical crops that are especially important in developing countries is shown in table 7.1. The growth of all these crops is sensitive to chilling (low but non-freezing temperatures) and, for root crops, temperatures below about 13°C cause acute storage problems. Root crops such as cassava, yams and sweet potatoes are staple foods in countries like Nigeria, Tanzania and parts of China. Cassava, for example, is the most perishable of all tropical crops but is the staple diet of 200–300 million people, mostly living at or close to subsistence level. It cannot be stored in the usual sense but is kept by leaving roots in the ground where they are vulnerable to any fall in soil temperature. Yam tubers are the staple diet for over 300 million people and contribute

Table 7.1 Annual world production of some tropical crops and their production in certain Third World countries[4]

| Crop | Production | | | | |
	World	Nigeria	Tanzania	India	China
All roots and tubers*	561.6	28.8	5.1	16.9	145.3
Cassava	127.3	11.0	4.7	5.8	3.3
Sweet potato	145.8	0.2	0.3	1.5	125.7
Sorghum	72.0	3.8	0.2	11.5	7.5
Rice	413.8	1.2	0.2	82.0	146.1
Population (millions)	4513.4	79.6	18.5	698.0	1007.8

Notes: Values for production are in millions of metric tonnes and all data relate to 1981. All these would be high-risk crops in a nuclear winter.
* This excludes potatoes.

up to half of the total calorific intake of the population in West Africa. Even today, about one million tonnes of yams are lost annually in storage and furthermore yams are very sensitive to chilling temperatures: tubers become damaged and inedible if the temperature falls below 10°C for more than a few days, and the lower the temperature, the sooner the damage occurs.

In 1984 the dreadful effects of famine in Ethiopia were plain to everyone and, without food aid and imports, that situation would have been reached two or three years earlier. During 1981, *before* harvests failed completely because of drought, the average amount of food consumed in Ethiopia amounted to only 1,729 calories per head, less than half the amount per head consumed in Western nations. Vegetable products comprised 91 per cent of Ethiopian food and in 13 other African countries the proportion was 95 per cent or more (in Western nations it was 65–70 per cent). This is why one failed harvest or even partial loss of food stocks brings starvation so quickly.

The loss of food aid and imports, the widespread destruction of current crops and stored food in nuclear winter conditions, and the possibility that new crops could not be planted until perhaps six months after the war, all point to famine in developing countries on a scale that is beyond imagination.

Almost inevitably, the starving populations of both developed and developing countries in the Northern and some parts of the Southern Hemisphere would turn to local foraging and try to find food 'in the wild'. Their prospects would be poor.

Exploiting Natural Ecosystems

Even in hunter–gatherer cultures where people are skilled foragers from natural ecosystems, food is often difficult to find. It would be very much more difficult for unskilled town dwellers. But additionally, after a nuclear war there could be the devastation caused to natural ecosystems by the nuclear winter.

If the effects predicted in chapter 6 occurred, then in the whole Northern Hemisphere there might be no plant growth for months, no harvest of wild fruits, few wild animals left to kill (apart from worms and other soil animals) and very limited reserves left in natural storage organs such as bulbs and tubers. Cutting down trees for fuel would probably become widespread in the developed countries (it is already common practice in developing countries) and the longer this continued, the longer it would take forests to recover. Prospects are especially bleak in the intensively cultivated areas of the temperate zone where there are few natural ecosystems left to exploit. The only obvious exception is the sea but, as pointed out in chapter 6, productivity here is likely to be low, accessibility difficult, and the catch from inshore fishing unsafe to eat. In the desperate situation facing survivors, however, the possibility of radioactive contamination would probably not deter hungry people from eating any food they could find.

A likely outcome is that starving survivors trying unsuccessfuly to find food in the countryside would plunder any remaining scraps from the agricultural ecosystems: animal feedstuff (in developed countries), surviving animal stock, and any seeds or tubers intended for sowing the next crop. Eating the seed corn has always been a problem in times of famine, and one which human societies have had to prevent in order to survive. It is a problem now, in 1985, in the drought-stricken Sahel area of Africa and it could be a much larger problem in the aftermath of a nuclear war. But in the long term, restoration of agriculture would be essential since natural ecosystems clearly could not provide sufficient food for human survivors.

The State of Agriculture after a Nuclear Winter

Crops

From what was said in chapter 6 it is clear that there would be almost no harvest in the Northern Hemisphere after a nuclear war in early summer. In the Southern Hemisphere there would probably also be poor harvests and some crop failures, caused by relatively small reductions in temperature and light. The final blow for crops struggling to survive could be shortage of water if, as seems likely, changed atmospheric conditions reduced rainfall. Crop production in a particular area is very closely linked to the supply of water from rain or irrigation. So arable land might remain bare and suscepti-ble to erosion for several months and areas exposed to heavy radioactive fallout (especially the kind released from targeted nuclear reactors) could be unusable for years.

Particularly worrying is the risk that global tempera-tures could remain a few degrees below average for perhaps 3–5 years *after* a nuclear war. Appendix 6.2 (chapter 6) illustrated how sensitive forests and grasslands are to this kind of change, but arable crops are even more sensitive. The major effect is that the length of the growing season is reduced to such an extent that, although a crop might grow, there is no yield of grain or tubers.

Worst affected are the marginal areas where the growing season is currently only just long enough to allow crops to mature: most of the grain belt in Canada and the USSR fall into this category. A fall in average tempera-ture of 1–2°C in these areas would have the effect of shifting the northern boundary for wheat growing about 150 kilometers further south, and this means a very large reduction in total wheat production. In Canada, for example, Robert Stewart has calculated that a fall of 1°C would reduce wheat production to 54 per cent of normal;[5]

production would be down to 6 per cent for a 2°C fall and zero for a fall of 3°C. Nor does the shift further south in the wheat growing belt allow land 'gained' in the south to compensate for land 'lost' in the north: differences in soil, rainfall or, indeed, lack of appropriate farming skills are likely to preclude this.

What crops can be harvested in particular places depends on a close coupling between climate and soil, and a fall in average temperature of a few degrees can powerfully affect this coupling. If such a change occurred now, without all the other problems caused by nuclear war, there would be world-wide agricultural chaos.

Animals

What about animal stock? Hardier types, such as beef cattle and sheep might be able to survive the cold without shelter. But since the grass would virtually stop growing for perhaps 9 months after a summer war, many of these animals would probably die of starvation (or be slaughtered) before warmer conditions returned. In many areas, farmers would be fortunate if 10 per cent survived.

Less hardy animals such as dairy cattle, pigs and chickens could almost certainly not survive prolonged cold without shelter and supplies of feed. Many are reared in intensive units that require a constant supply of power for ventilation and temperature control. Water supplies would be critical and many farmers carry food stocks for pigs and poultry sufficient to last only for a few days or, at most, weeks. These animals have little ability to forage naturally and low resistance to cold, so they could not possibly survive for long if released into a cold, wintry environment.

Think of the problems that would arise in trying to maintain even a small dairy herd in the UK during a nuclear winter. If a war happened in summer, the herd could be brought indoors only if hay or silage had been harvested, otherwise they would have to be left outdoors. Either way, they would have to be milked by hand in the absence of electrical power and, assuming that were possible, what would be done with the milk? There would be no tankers calling to collect it. In some areas milk would also be unfit for human consumption because of radioactive contamination, although, as with contaminated food supplies, hungry people would probably drink the milk regardless.

A massive, centrally-organized operation would be needed to improve the situation. It would involve transfer of (skilled) workers to farms; hand-milking (with careful monitoring for radioactivity); conversion of most milk to cheese or butter for storage; and slaughter and distribution of sick or surplus animals. There seem to be no plans for such an operation and, even if they existed, the chances of success are slim. The odds are that the farmer would feed and milk only the few animals needed to support his or her family and a few local residents and refugees. There would be no dairy produce for the rest of the population and few dairy cattle left from which to build up herds at the end of twelve months of wintry conditions.

Is it realistic, however, to hope that farmers might start to sow crops and breed animals after the worst of a nuclear winter were over? *Would* agriculture recover?

Agricultural recovery

We have already discussed how even the small reductions in average temperature (and probably rainfall) predicted for a few years after a nuclear war could reduce the yield of crops very severely. But poor crop growth would not be the only problem hindering agricultural recovery. The advanced agriculture that produces much of the world's food today is more like the car industry than old-fashioned farming. It is highly mechanized, requires a relatively small workforce and depends on high inputs of, amongst other things: fertilizers, herbicides, pesticides, fuel for machinery, water for irrigation in some areas, power, water and food concentrates for intensive animal units. Modern agriculture is, therefore, so heavily dependent on technological support that recovery to anything like pre-war levels would be impossible without it.

But technological support systems — the factories that make fertilizers and the fuel and power supplies for machinery — would be largely destroyed by a nuclear war and *they* could not recover if there were no food to support their workforce or fuel for machinery. The likely outcome would be reversion of agriculture to some pre-technological phase and it would be a very primitive kind of substistence farming: in the UK we would lack the tools and skills even to farm as efficiently as mediaeval peasants.

One problem, finding seed for crops and animals fit to breed, has already been mentioned. If this could be overcome, the next problem would be shortage of labour and basic equipment for cultivation. Without fuel, modern farm equipment would be useless and there are no working horses or hand-operated ploughs on modern farms. It also takes about 100 times more people to farm without modern machinery and about three-fifths of the surviving populations would need to work on the land in order to feed everybody. This is roughly the proportion of agricultural workers in mediaeval England. But after a nuclear war it is quite probable that at least two out of five people would be too ill, too old or too young to work on the land and this means that there would be virtually no people available to do anything *other* than produce food. Unlike mediaeval peasants, however, few people in modern, developed societies have any knowledge of agriculture, so the prospect after a nuclear war is of an unskilled, poorly-equipped workforce attempting to raise food *by hand* under extremely difficult conditions. A rapid agricultural recovery is clearly out of the question.

Small-scale, subsistence agriculture is all that would be possible for some years after a nuclear war. Conditions for plant growth would be poor for at least two or three years, with abnormal patterns of rainfall and temperature in the Northern Hemisphere, soils impoverished by erosion, and possible problems from increased UV-B radiation. Furthermore, modern varieties of crops compete poorly with weeds and are often highly susceptible to pests, yet there would be no herbicides, pesticides or fungicides to protect them. Weeds are among the plants most likely to regenerate after a nuclear winter; fungal pathogens could have persisted as spores; and there is a fairly high chance that among surviving insects would be pest species with a capacity for rapid increase. Post-war agriculture might, therefore, be dominated by weeds, pests and diseases.

It could take years to restore agriculture in the developed countries even to nineteenth-century standards and advanced, twentieth-century agriculture might never be restored. Without fertilizers and hybrid seeds, the gains in production brought about in some Third World countries by the 'Green Revolution' would vanish. The inevitable result would be years of hunger and starvation throughout the world.

Longer-Term Health Problems

Although shortage of food could be the most widespread and serious problem among human survivors, poor health would certainly be another. For several years after a nuclear war, chronic and acute health problems are predicted. These would arise from a combination of three main factors: the breakdown of medical and public-health services; the effects of world-wide pollution with radio-isotopes and of early exposure to fallout immediately after the attacks; and, probably the most important factor, the spread of epidemic diseases, mainly because of poor living conditions, malnutrition, lack of sanitation and severe psychological stress. We consider each of these factors separately although they would, of course, act together with powerful synergistic effects.

Collapse of Medical and Public-Health Services

Several analyses, including that published by the British Medical Association in 1983,[6] have predicted a rapid collapse of medical services in countries such as the UK. The loss of hospitals and medically trained people would have long-term effects in the target areas and virtual destruction of the pharmaceutical industry would have world-wide repercussions. There are no large stockpiles of pharmaceutical products, and vaccines and vital drugs, including antibiotics, are manufactured by a relatively small number of firms. Nearly all of these are in target countries. Indeed, according to one authority the pharmaceutical industry will be specifically targeted for maximum destruction in a nuclear war.[7]

Without drugs and technological support, modern medicine would disintegrate as rapidly as modern agriculture. During the first weeks after a nuclear attack, when the need for acute medical care would be greater than ever before, doctors would be able to do little except provide basic first aid for a small proportion of the injured who could get to them. In the months and years that followed the spread of epidemic disease and the chronic effects of radiation would be the major problems and, without drugs or vaccines, very little could be done. Herbal medicines might be of some help if people had the knowledge to use them properly; but, at least in the north temperate zone, it is uncertain whether herbal plants would have survived a nuclear winter.

More people in the world today owe their lives to good public-health measures than to sophisticated medical care. Provision of clean water and food, of safe sewage disposal (especially in cities) and of vaccination programmes has virtually eliminated the old killer diseases from developed countries and led to great improvements in developing countries. After a nuclear war, all these services would collapse and, in the long term, more lives might be lost through the breakdown of public-health services than through the loss of hospitals.

Radiation

Damage to health caused by exposure to radiation (i.e. ionizing radiation emitted by the radio-isotopes produced during nuclear explosions) is one of the most feared consequences of nuclear war. You cannot see or feel radiation but a high dose may cause death within hours and there is no such thing as a 'safe' dose, even if the effects are not apparent until years later.

Most people who received a radiation dose of 400 to 800 rads within a few days of a nuclear attack would die in a matter of weeks from radiation sickness, especially with virtually no medical aid available and cold, stressful conditions. These short term effects of radiation are fully described in *The medical effects of nuclear war* (note 6, chapter 7) and we shall not discuss them here. But over the next few months, the entire population in the northern mid-latitudes would receive a substantial dose of radiation, calculated to average at least 50 rads.[8] This could come from handling, breathing in, or consuming radioactive material and at least one person in 160 receiving this dose might expect to die within 5 to 30 years from radiation-induced cancer.[9] Fertility would be reduced, especially among men, because even 10 rads can depress sperm production for up to a year and 250 rads can cause sterility for three years or more.

As global fallout from the clouds of dust and smoke contaminated more of the Northern and Southern Hemis-

pheres, more people would receive low doses of radiation, mainly from the food and water they consumed.
The effects on human health would not be immediate or
dramatic. Rather there would be an increased *risk* of
cancer (especially leukaemia and among children in
particular), of cataracts and of foetal abnormalities which
would lead in most cases to death and abortion of the
foetus rather than to the birth of deformed children.

Certain habits and diets might increase the human
intake of dangerous radio-isotopes because of the way
that these are concentrated along food chains. People
eating meat, for example might accumulate radioactive
caesium (caesium-137), which concentrates in muscle
tissue. This concentration has been investigated for
eskimos and lapps in the lichen-caribou-human food
chain. Here the concentration of caesium-137 in caribou
meat is 2 to 6 times greater than in lichens and 0.5 to 2.4
times greater in humans than in caribou. The human
variation depends partly on when the caribou are killed
because their caesium-137 content is highest in spring
after a winter diet of lichens. In places such as Alaska,
spring-killed animals are traditionally stored and eaten
throughout the summer,[10] so this practice increases
greatly the human intake of radioactivity. A diet rich in
fish might also be risky because iron-55, another long-
lived radio-isotope, is very strongly concentrated in both
marine and freshwater food chains to levels around 1,000
times greater than those of any other isotope.

Another point relevant to human health is that both
ionizing radiation and UV-B radiation tend to suppress
the immune system. This elaborate defence system
protects the body against infection, so that any weakening
of it increases the risk of serious illness from even quite
mild ailments. Given the lack of drugs and doctors, this
could be an especially serious problem.

For healthy, well-fed people today, the long-term
radiation hazards seem a chilling prospect. And yet
compared with the numbers who are likely to die from

starvation and epidemic disease after a nuclear war, radiation presents a relatively *minor* risk.

Epidemic Disease: Stress and Poor Living Conditions

Epidemic disease almost invariably accompanies famine and major natural disasters. Within target areas, the breakdown of public health services, lack of sanitation, restriction (and often contamination) of water supplies and generally dirty conditions would probably cause outbreaks of food poisoning and diarrhoea within a few weeks. Figure 7.1 shows the incidence predicted for the US after a nuclear war and the incidence in Europe would probably be similar. The 1983 report from the British Medical Association urged:

> It is of prime importance that the general public should attempt to ensure as high a standard of personal hygiene and food handling as is possible in a nuclear emergency and that the public should avoid faecal contamination of food, which is likely to be consumed cold in the absence of cooking facilities in shelter conditions.[12]

This is undoubtedly sound advice but few of the distraught survivors would be able to follow it. Not only would conditions be cold and dark with damaged houses and no public-health services, but many survivors would also be in a state of severe shock.

The psychological effects on survivors in the target zone can only be guessed at, although experience from the Japanese atom bomb attacks and from natural disasters provides some parallels. There would be widespread apathy: people who had lost everything might simply not care what became of themselves and take no active steps to ensure self-preservation. Others might be demented

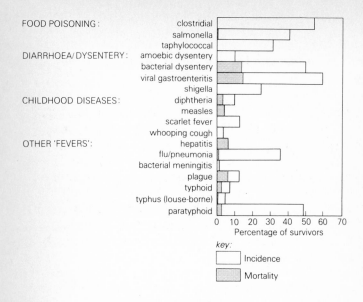

Figure 7.1. Epidemic diseases likely to affect the US population during the first year after a nuclear war[11]

Note: These figures assume no medical countermeasures.

with grief or anger and some would be overcome by fear. Above all, people would not behave rationally.

Food poisoning and diarrhoea might not sound very serious but they can be lethal for people who are weak, old or very young — especially if water is in short supply and rehydration by simple sugar and salt solution is unavailable. Over 500 million children are affected annually by diarrhoea at present and about 20 per cent of these die.

Living conditions would still be appalling after people in target areas emerged from shelters and, as they began to move around more freely and as people in non-target areas began to feel the effects of food shortages, world-wide epidemics of cholera, dysentery and typhoid are predicted. These are classic, famine-related diseases and even today they are killers. In December 1984, 5,000 people were stricken with cholera in one district of Bangladesh and 500 died. For people experiencing a nuclear winter and weakened by cold, malnutrition and psychological stress, the death toll coud be much higher.

As warmer conditions returned the risk of other epidemics would increase. Many of these epidemics (see figure 7.1) have been controlled for years in developed countries by public-health measures, high standards of living and vaccination. Without these controls, diseases linked with poverty, malnutrition and overcrowding would go unchecked. Measles and polio could spread among unvaccinated children. Tuberculosis, the 'Great White Plague' of the nineteenth century would almost certainly increase. And there are even predictions that bubonic plague, the mediaeval 'Black Death' could return (note 11, chapter 7). This highly infectious disease once devastated European populations and is still endemic in the US. It is carried by rat fleas — and rats are one of the few species likely to increase after a nuclear war, despite the effects of any nuclear winter. Without the usual control measures, the populations of rats and some disease-carrying insects could expand rapidly, bringing plague and possibly malaria and typhus.

Many of the epidemic diseases listed in figure 7.1 have taken years to control. Others are still common but rarely lethal for well-fed and generally healthy populations. All that could change after a nuclear war, especially if followed by nuclear winter and years of famine. In terms of human health it would be a return to the Dark Ages.

The Total Cost

People have known for a long time that the immediate effects of a nuclear war would cause terrible suffering in the combatant nations. What is now clear is tht this would be only the beginning. The longer-term effects — destruction of the environment, spread of epidemic disease, contamination by radioactivity and, most of all, collapse of agriculture — would spread famine and death to every country.

Evidence from history and anthropology shows time, and time again, that societies or civilisations have a point of no return: if more than 50 per cent of their population is destroyed, then usually they cannot recover and the social fabric disintegrates for good.[13] What that means, in human terms, is the loss of everything except a primitive instinct to find food and stay alive. Money would be irrelevant. Art, music and literature would disappear. Everything that gives meaning, purpose and dignity to life would be gone.

The risk of destroying 'civilization' is high and many people would call it a certainty. But there is a risk beyond even this. It is small but finite and, for the first time, has to be considered. The gobal effects of nuclear war and nuclear winter could be so severe and weaken human populations so much that the human species might not survive at all. If it happened this would probably be a gradual fading away over many years rather than a sudden event.

The basic causes would be fragmentation of weakened populations coupled with disease and lack of food. People are likely to form relatively isolated groups, each concerned only with obtaining food and with their own survival. Small isolated populations of any species are in danger of extinction. In recent years, isolated tribes of Amazonian Indians have been wiped out by introduced epidemic diseases and it is just possible that, one group at a time, survivors of a nuclear war could suffer a similar fate. The ultimate cost of a nuclear war could be human extinction.

8 Policy Implications

The recent research outlined in this book shows that the combination of the Earth's climatic system and the nuclear weapons stockpile might be a *Doomsday machine*.

Readers who have seen the film *Dr Strangelove* have already come across the notion of a Doomsday machine. It is a hypothetical device whose only function is to automatically destroy most, if not all, human life if ever deterrence fails. The classic machine would be wired to go off as soon as nuclear weapons detonate over the homeland. The so-called *Doomsday-in-a-hurry* version would be triggered by a lesser provocation such as an attack on an ally. At first sight such devices would seem to be the ultimate deterrent.

The concept of a Doomsday machine was formulated by Herman Kahn, a strategist and systems analyst working at the RAND Corporation in the USA.[1] Writing in 1960, Kahn thought that the device would probably involve 'the creation of really large amounts of radioactivity or the *causing of major climatic changes* or, less likely, the extreme use of thermal effects'.[2] At the time the most likely candidate seemed to be a giant cobalt bomb which, when detonated, would send vast quantities of long-lived radioactive cobalt around the world.

Kahn considered whether a Doomsday machine might be built inadvertently, but ruled it out on the grounds that decision makers were now alerted to the possibility and would make sure it never happened.[3] Now it looks as if he might have been proven wrong in this last respect. If the recent scientific research is even approximately correct, there have been more than enough nuclear weapons to trigger a climatic catastrophe since the late 1950s.

Unlike the classic Doomsday device, nuclear winter is not an inevitable consequence of nuclear war. It is only a possibility, and the triggering mechanism is complex and poorly understood. Nevertheless the similarities are striking. Humankind might have built itself a Doomsday machine over a quarter of a century ago without even realizing it.

This raises some key questions. How should we react to this possibility? What implications should it have for public policy and personal action? This chapter sets out to provide some initial answers.

The Worse it would Be, the Safer it Is?

It could be argued that the possibility of nuclear winter merely strengthens the policy of nuclear deterrence. Like the Doomsday machine, the threat of nuclear winter has at least two of the characteristics of an ideal deterrent. It is as frightening as anything could be, and it should ensure that even an idiot will be vividly aware of the risk of world destruction. What could be a more effective deterrent?

This argument would be irrefutable if we lived in a world in which nothing went wrong and if all leaders took only rational decisions and were fully aware of their potential implications. However, our world is different: nobody with any knowledge of history or experience of real institutions can believe that all events are under such control. This being the case, defence policies should be chosen according to the risks involved.

A policy's *risk* depends on two factors: the *chance* of

the policy going wrong and the damage, or *cost*, that would result if it did. If the possible cost is very great, a policy could be unacceptable even if the chance of it going wrong is very small.

Although people often use the words 'risk' and 'chance' as if they were interchangeable, everybody intuitively takes account of the distinction in their everyday decisions. Many people are prepared to bet £1 on a 50–50 chance, but hardly anybody is prepared to play russian roulette even though there is a better chance of winning (better than 5 in 6). The reason is that losing £1 is easier to countenance than blowing one's brains out.

What is the risk of nuclear deterrence? No one can claim there is no chance of nuclear war. As indicated in chapter two, there are all too many ways in which such a war could start. So our attitude towards nuclear deterrence should depend on whether we are prepared to accept its potential costs.

Many people, including the present authors, believe that the risk of killing 'just' several hundred-million people is unacceptable. Even before the nuclear winter predictions, they believed that the risks of present nuclear policies were much too high and that nuclear disarmament was therefore an urgent priority.

However, nuclear policy makers in the Warsaw Pact and NATO countries do not behave as if they agree with us. The developing nuclear arsenals and the preparations for nuclear war are strong evidence that these people promote and administer policies for which, in extreme circumstances, such losses are acceptable.

The nuclear winter predictions show that they have been risking much more than they thought.

A global nuclear war followed by nuclear winter would lead to the deaths of billions of people. It is inconceivable that civil defence could do anything to prevent this. Many of the different species of life on the planet, and possibly a majority of 'higher' (such as mammal or bird) species, would be made extinct. Human civilization would be irrevocably changed and could well be destroyed. For the first time, biologists cannot rule out the possibility of human extinction.

This means that decision makers in the nuclear weapon states have been gambling with the whole of humanity. More is at stake even than the human present. The loss of civilization would rob the past of meaning and future generations of the possibility of a humane existence. In human terms the possible costs of present policies are effectively infinite.

It is fundamentally unethical for any group of people to be in a position to risk so much. Purely in terms of pragmatism, it is enormously foolhardy to allow them to continue to gamble in this way.

Uncertainties

There are real uncertainties involved in the nuclear winter predictions. They are based on models of poorly-understood processes. Many of the complex scientific problems will take many years to resolve and some of the key uncertainties will remain unless there is a nuclear war. Science cannot provide certainty on this issue. However, one doesn't require certainty to take decisions about risks.

Manufacturers of dangerous chemicals have to show that there is no significant risk of a catastrophic accident. People who object to the prospect of living around the site of a chemical plant are not required to prove that such an accident is inevitable: if the risk is high, the plant should not be built.

Nevertheless, with chemical plants people can live with some chance of an accident. In this case, humanity can learn from its past mistakes. With nuclear winter there would be no second chance. The potential costs are so enormous that it hardly matters for our argument whether the probability that the nuclear winter predictions are basically correct is 10 per cent, 50 per cent, or 90 per cent. As the report of the Royal Society of Canada said: 'We conclude that the nuclear winter hypothesis does indeed modify the global strategic position . . . At some point the strategists have to accept the probability of the predicted consequences, and incorporate that judgement into this thinking.'[4]

The risk of a nuclear winter means that the present nuclear weapon arsenals are unacceptable.

What should be Done?

Granted that the possibility of nuclear winter undermines present nuclear weapons policies, how should they be changed?

The fundamental task, in our view, is to ensure that no nuclear war can occur at all by securing verified complete global nuclear disarmament, while reducing the role of military force in international relations. However that can only be achieved, if at all, as a result of a long process. So in the first instance, the nuclear winter predictions mean that we must ensure that any nuclear war would not trigger climatic catastrophe.

One conceivable approach would be for the nuclear weapon states to agree to limit the scale of any nuclear war and only to target areas where few urban and forest fires would be ignited.

The inadequacy of this approach is obvious. Even if the states could come to an agreement, it is doubtful that it would be adhered to in war. In any case, most experts judge that a limited nuclear war between East and West would almost certainly escalate uncontrollably. The only way of ensuring that a nuclear war would not result in nuclear winter is to drastically reduce the stockpiles of nuclear weapons to below some 'threshold' level.

The scale of nuclear war sufficient to trigger nuclear

winter is uncertain (see chapter 5). It depends on the season, the targets, and on many other factors. Nuclear exchanges of only a few hundred megatons could be enough in the unlikely event that they were concentrated on cities. At the other extreme, a 2,000 megaton nuclear war would cause only mild changes of climate if the attacks could be confined to missile silos and bomber airfields.

So, there is no well-defined threshold for the size of nuclear arsenals below which nuclear winter could not occur. However, as far as we can tell at present, the risk of triggering a climatic catastrophe would be very significantly reduced if the world's nuclear stockpiles contained a yield of less than one or two thousand megatons. It seems sensible to set the threshold at this level. The higher the number of warheads is above this threshold, the more likely it is that nuclear war would result in the catastrophe described in this book.

Most people would agree that the nuclear arsenals should be reduced substantially, but it is sobering to consider just how deeply cuts need to be made to avoid the risk of nuclear winter. Figure 8.1 compares the approximate threshold with the growth of the stockpile of strategic weapons alone. It is inspired by a graph in an excellent article by Professor Carl Sagan on the implications of the nuclear winter predictions.[5]

The *strategic* warhead stockpile is already ten times greater than the approximate nuclear winter threshold. If present deployment plans go ahead, this stockpile is set to increase even further in the next decade. Even if the most radical disarmament proposals (such as the 'deep cuts' proposal by George Kennan and Noel Gayler)[6] were successfully negotiated and followed through without a hitch, the strategic nuclear arsenal would not be reduced to below the threshold until the beginning of the next century.

In addition to the strategic weapons, there are about 31,000 tactical and theatre warheads, and over 1,000

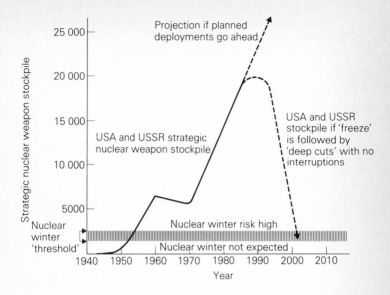

Figure 8.1. Strategic nuclear stockpiles and the threshold for nuclear winter

Note: From C. Sagan, note 5, chapter 8. © Carl Sagan, 1984.

warheads held by France, China and the UK. All these are also set to increase. Finally, if present trends continue, more countries are likely to acquire nuclear weapons, making it harder to secure disarmament agreements that reduce and hold the total world nuclear stockpiles below the nuclear winter threshold.

Taking all this into account it is clear that the necessary cuts are immense, and the task of achieving them will be even harder if they are not urgently applied. It is doubtful that we can afford to wait until the next century to remove the risk of nuclear winter. Logic now demands that much more radical disarmament proposals are tabled and acted upon.

Recently, however, even modest attempts at limiting the *growth* of the nuclear arsenals have seemed ambitious. Are policy makers likely to rise to the challenge and reverse the arms race now that they have fuller information about the risks?

Nuclear Policies

In the 1960s, military and political leaders were virtually unanimous in rejecting the construction of a Doomsday machine. Kahn, who argued for a first-strike capability and plans for limited nuclear war and was no liberal on these issues, confessed to great relief that no general or politician wanted to make out a 'General Operating Requirement' for the device. Only a few scientists in the nuclear weapons laboratories, the Dr Strangeloves of the period, seemed keen on the idea.

On the face of it, this should make us optimistic that they will apply the same clear logic to our present situation and will dismantle, without prompting, the Doomsday machine that they have inadvertently built. However, it is much easier to reject a device that is not yet constructed than a vast complex of weapons systems that already exist. Removing the threat of nuclear winter does not mean dismantling just one or two devices. It would involve thoroughgoing changes in all nuclear weapons policy.

Several hundred nuclear warheads are quite enough for a policy of Mutual Assured Destruction (MAD). Many would think that the ability to obliterate all of the opponents cities with a population of more than half a million people (the USSR has about 50 such cities) would be enough to deter the most warlike of adversaries. However, neither the USA, NATO, or USSR use the MAD doctrine as a basis for nuclear planning and its is doubtful that they ever have done. They prefer to prepare their nuclear weapons as if they could be used for more traditional political and military objectives (see chapter 2).

In fact nuclear weapons are deployed to deter conventional attacks and attacks on allies, as well as nuclear attacks on the homeland. For example NATO strategy explicitly envisages the first use of nuclear weapons if the Warsaw Pact seemed to be winning a conventional war in Europe. If nuclear war starts, each side plans to fight it according to some military rationality, thus generating a need for large arsenals of highly sophisticated nuclear hardware. All this is even worse than the classic Doomsday machine. More than anything else, the present system resembles Kahn's Doomsday-in-a-hurry device.

Pre-Nuclear Age Ideas

One fundamental obstacle to change is that decision makers and others often seem to find it hard to abandon ideas that are inappropriate to the nuclear age.

In the absence of nuclear weapons wars can be won. The consequences of conventional wars are terrible, but many people can benefit from them. In Britain the poor were better fed during World War Two than in the decade before, and there was a sense of unity that has not been felt since. As a nation, the USA emerged from the war more prosperous and powerful than when it began, though the central Europeans, Russians and Jews, were less fortunate. Before, during and after conventional wars, many arms manufacturers prosper. Together with the bulk of the political and military leaders, they often have little to fear for their personal safety. In short, although conventional wars cause great death and destruction, it *is* possible to fight them to some rational purpose.

A large-scale thermonuclear war would be different. There could be no victory; at best there is only the hope of slightly less total defeat than the adversary. Now the nuclear winter shows that everybody is at risk, even those who live far from the combatant nations. Yet nuclear forces are developed and deployed as if little had changed: as if they could, *in extremis*, be used to some advantage. New weapons are introduced in the interests of 'parity' or 'superiority' although the nuclear arsenals of both nuclear alliances have long passed the point at which numbers make much difference to their capability to obliterate any opponent. In a world of mutual nuclear 'overkill', concern for balance is a relic from a pre-nuclear age.

A slightly more sophisticated obstacle to nuclear weapon cuts is the idea that although parity or superiority would not be important in conducting a nuclear war, they *are* important to deterrence. This rests on the belief that in a confrontation the side with the largest and most elaborate nuclear arsenal will be able to bluff more self-confidently and force the other to back down, even though it possesses no real advantage at all.

Once defence is seen to rest on symbols of power that are so disconnected from reality as these, the floodgates are opened. All kinds of amateur psychology can be substituted for serious analysis of how to improve security. In many cases, this is indeed what has happened.

The threat of nuclear war can be used to deter, but this can only be done effectively at the price of risking nuclear war itself. The winner, if there is one, of this game of chicken would be the side that behaves most recklessly, not necessarily the one with the largest nuclear arsenal. If neither side backs down, all humanity loses.

One real lesson of the nuclear age is that neither nuclear alliance can be secure unless the other is. Increasing the insecurity of an opponent simply increases the chance of war by accident or misperception. In this context, nuclear cuts towards the nuclear winter threshold make everybody safer, even if the adversary does not immediately reciprocate. The uncooperative adversary gains no useful military advantage and risks enormous political setbacks. The chance of nuclear war is reduced, and the risk of nuclear winter if war does occur is lessened.

The logic of cutting the nuclear arsenals, at least to the nuclear winter threshold, seems unanswerable. But it is clear that removing the threat of nuclear winter really would involve fundamental challenges to present policies. The new research into the effects of nuclear war on the climate could help to jolt people's ideas about security into the nuclear age. However, the obstacles to change do not lie only in the realm of ideas.

Leaders and the 'Doomsday System'

It would have been easier to avoid the threat of nuclear winter if the risks had become clear thirty years ago, while the stockpiles were relatively small. As it is, despite some early hints, scientists took until 1982 to appreciate the possibility of climatic catastrophe. Now it is much more difficult. Immense political, bureaucratic, military, scientific, and industrial institutions are deeply involved in the nuclear weapons 'system', making it much harder to institute change.

People who help to run this 'system' cannot be expected to view the implications of nuclear winter with the objectivity of outsiders. Although much of the preceding argument was based on assessments of risk, we all know that people often do not approach decisions so rationally, especially when their status, power, income and career, and the interests of their own institution or political group, are involved. The nuclear arms race itself shows vividly how decision makers tend to be influenced much more strongly by immediate political, institutional, ideological and economic pressures, than by long-term rationality.

So it is no surprise that some military and political

figures, instead of accepting its fundamental implications, are already beginning to use the risk of nuclear winter to support aspects of the arms race. It is beginning to be used as an argument in favour of planning for 'sub-threshold' limited nuclear wars; developing new warheads (which have relatively small fire zones) for accurate missiles like the Pershing II; and developing Ballistic Missile Defence systems (such as those envisaged in the so-called 'star wars' schemes) which could intercept incoming warheads before they can start fires.

None of these programmes represent a rational response to the risk of nuclear winter. Plans for limited nuclear war foster dangerous delusions and, in the event, are unlikely to prevent escalation to large-scale war. New, accurate warheads further destabilize the present precarious situation and are, in any case, stockpiled together with great numbers of older or larger yield warheads which could cause vast fire zones. The Strategic Defence Initiative (Star Wars) plan is unlikely to work and threatens to provoke further increases in the number of offensive weapons. Far from being solutions, such proposals are a part of the problem.

It is not even entirely clear that knowledge of the risk of nuclear winter will prevent leaders from opting for pre-emptive nuclear strikes in the midst of a crisis. A full-scale pre-emptive strike could trigger a catastrophic nuclear winter even if there were no retaliation. But if war seemed to be inevitable, leaders would have to weigh the balance between two options: devastation plus nuclear winter if the other side strikes first; or less devastation plus nuclear winter if 'we' strike first. In spite of the 'overkill' of the present nuclear arsenals, many could regard it as rational to prefer the second option to the first.

The risk of a nuclear winter may be enough to persuade some decision makers to risk their career and status in an attempt to achieve substantial nuclear disarmament. Many others will have private doubts. But we reluctantly conclude that, without outside pressure, there is little hope that a sufficient number of people in the relevant positions of power will act to achieve the deep cuts that are so urgently required.

Outside Pressures

However, the cuts might be achieved if people were to intervene and create a climate of opinion in which the necessary changes can be forced through. If policy makers respond to direct pressure rather than long-term rationality, then people must act to ensure that the pressures towards armament are more than counterbalanced by those for cuts in the nuclear stockpiles.

Until recently there did not seem to be much hope that this could be achieved, but since the end of the 1970s concern about nuclear issues has widened and deepened. Questions that were previously discussed quietly amongst a small number of 'experts' are now widely debated. People are becoming better informed and less willing to allow decisions to be made about nuclear weapons without public scrutiny.

The possibility of nuclear winter, in addition to the previously-known dangers of nuclear policies, could help this process to develop. It is changing many people's minds about the wisdom of present nuclear weapons policy. Many other people have been stimulated to act where previously they have left discussions about their defence and security to others. More people would probably do likewise if they believed that they could have an effect and if they had decided what sort of actions should be taken — issues that are addressed in the concluding chapter of this book.

9 The Nuclear Winter — A Threat and a Challenge

The risks involved in nuclear policies have been known for many years to be high. Even without a climatic catastrophe, a nuclear war could kill over a billion people, tear apart the social fabric in the combatant nations, and change human civilization beyond recognition. Now it appears that the stakes have been even higher. The threat of nuclear winter introduces some qualitatively new dangers, and thereby brings a new dimension and a new urgency to the nuclear debate.

The best available scientific evidence now indicates that:

- The arsenals of nuclear weapons, combined with the Earth's climatic system, constitute an unreliable Doomsday machine.
- Our whole environment could at least temporarily become a victim of a nuclear war. Much of the Earth's land surface could become dark and cold for months.
- The dark and cold could devastate most neutral countries, even those far from the conflict. In comparison, the previously known hazard from global radioactive fallout would pale into insignificance.
- Starvation and disease could become the major killers as harvests failed in nearly all of the Northern Hemisphere and, possibly, many parts of the Southern Hemisphere.

• Many plant and animal species on Earth, and perhaps the majority of 'higher' species such as mammals and birds, could be made extinct.
• The possibility of human extinction can no longer be ruled out.

On the basis of present scientific understanding, there is a strong chance of a nuclear winter following a large-scale thermonuclear war. The uncertainties are real, but they might go either way; the nuclear winter could turn out to be much milder (particularly after a winter war) or much more severe than the present best estimates. Calculations indicate a climatic catastrophe even if reasonably conservative assumptions are made.

The predicted effects will probably be adjusted and refined as the uncertainties are reduced by further research. However, some of the scientific issues will remain unresolved unless there is the 'final experiment' of nuclear war. At any given time, science can only provide the best evidence available. It could not provide certainty on this question until it was too late. So there is no excuse for refusing an immediate reassessment of the risks involved in nuclear weapons policy.

Once the risks are examined, it becomes clear that changes are required. It would be rash and immoral to continue to gamble with the future of humanity. The logic of cutting the nuclear arsenals to at least the nuclear threshold seems unassailable.

Apart from a few short intervals, the superpowers have been engaged in arms control or disarmament negotiations for over twenty years. Some useful agreements have been concluded, and even where the results have been disappointing the very process of negotiation has helped to improve understanding. Yet it must be recognized that none of these negotiations has done much more than divert or channel the nuclear arms race. Any serious attempt to remove the risk of nuclear winter must take account of this past experience.

The failure to halt and reverse the nuclear build-up is not because such an objective is against the national interests of the states involved. Whatever their conflicts, every state has a fundamental interest in radically reducing the nuclear stockpiles. Rather it seems to be because pre-nuclear age issues, as outlined in chapter 8, have been allowed to dominate. Instead of seeking common ground, small points of detail and unimportant inbalances have often been highlighted in order to adopt hard bargaining positions. Worse, the introduction of new weapons has regularly been justified as a way of coercing the other side into concessions which, it is promised, will lead to disarmament sometime in the future. This approach has never succeeded in reversing the arms race. The new weapons have not been bargained away and their introduction has provoked the other side into deploying their own new weapons.

If negotiations are ever to succeed in removing the threat of nuclear winter, the idea that they can be regarded as a way of securing unilateral advantage must be abandoned. At the very least, new weapons should not be developed or deployed while the negotiations are in progress. Such restraint would increase trust and avoid the danger of the final treaty being undermined by new technical developments. In view of the vast overkill of the present arsenals, there would be little risk and potentially important advantages for one side to freeze, if not cut back, its nuclear arsenal even if the other side does not immediately reciprocate. This would break the rules of the usual game, but it is vital that negotiators stop acting as if they were preparing for another World War Two and start to acknowledge the realities and risks of the nuclear age.

The present levels of overkill give each side wide areas of manoeuvre for disarmament initiatives. If nuclear policy makers are unlikely to make use of this on their own, then everybody must take the responsibility. It seems that a massive outside intervention is required in order to create a new climate of opinion in which the necessary changes can be made. The pressures for change can come from people living in countries within the nuclear alliances and from non-nuclear countries outside of the nuclear blocks. Both are potentially important, yet each is in a different situation.

Outside the Nuclear Alliances

The nuclear arms race has continued without much reference to the views of non-nuclear states outside of NATO and the Warsaw Pact. Most governments of these countries clearly view nuclear weapons with alarm. By deciding not to build their own nuclear weapons, countries such as Sweden have played an important role in slowing the pace of proliferation. However, although many resolutions urging nuclear disarmament have been passed at international organizations such as the United Nations, only a few countries have pursued nuclear disarmament as a consistently high priority.

The problem of nuclear weapons must have seemed very distant to many of these countries. The studies showing the catastrophic effects that a nuclear war would have on trade, the economy, and agriculture, must have seemed abstract to many people. The effects of darkness and sudden cooling on most of the populated world are much easier to imagine. Now it is clear that everybody is involved. Life on Earth could be even more interconnected and vulnerable than we thought.

As they became aware of the dangers of global radioactive fallout from nuclear weapons' tests in the atmosphere, the non-nuclear states exerted strong influence in securing the Partial Test Ban Treaty in 1964. The threat of climatic catastrophe could jolt these countries into making the reduction of the nuclear arsenals a high-priority goal. Though they are, for the most part, relatively weak economically, together these nations have the potential to wield significant political influence. After all, much of the contest between the superpowers is aimed at winning friends and influence with the governments of these countries.

However many inhabitants of Asia, Africa, and Latin America, are inevitably preoccupied with the problems of day-to-day survival. The governments of these societies, and of more prosperous countries like Sweden, Japan, New Zealand or Australia, will, it is hoped, be prompted by the new research to make nuclear cuts a priority. Several are already taking a lead. But a large part of the responsibility for change must rest on the people living inside the nuclear alliances.

Inside the Nuclear Alliances

Most people in the two nuclear blocks have had little more influence over their government's decisions about nuclear weapons than citizens of the developing countries. This is not inevitable. In many cases people have failed even to try to affect policy.

Even in the more democratic countries, groups of people who try to provoke a public debate about defence policy are often regarded with deep suspicion. An atmosphere has been created where it sometimes seems even unprofessional for scientists and others to become concerned with the broader implications of their work. After many years in which nuclear policy went largely undebated in Europe and elsewhere, it is only recently that large numbers of people have started to take responsibility for present policies and to look for ways of changing them.

Issues related to national security are often shrouded in unnecessary secrecy, which can be used to block debates on matters that affect everyone's prospects for survival.

People have a right to know the facts about nuclear policy and new developments, and since it is impossible to change opinion without a well-informed public, asserting this right is an intrinsic part of the process leading to nuclear disarmament.

On its own, public opinion has little effect on decisions unless it is associated with action. If, as discussed in chapter 8, decision makers are more affected by direct and immediate pressures than by long-term rationality, then those pressures must be generated. A wide range of institutions are involved in decisions about nuclear weapons, so the ways in which pressure can be exerted vary enormously. But for most people the most effective and obvious aim is to influence politicians. Whatever kind of government a country may have, its political leaders are affected to some degree by popular opinion. The more open and democratic a country is, the greater is this influence and the greater is the responsibility to exert it.

As the risks become more widely appreciated there will perhaps be broad agreement about the importance of reducing the nuclear arsenals to at least the nuclear winter threshold. Inevitably, the means of achieving such reductions will be much more controversial. It would be foolish for us to try to produce some sort of blueprint for change. People must come to their own decision and use any peaceful means that seem appropriate.

The threat of climatic catastrophe is so awful that it can produce a profound pessimism and a paralysis of the will to fight against it. It sometimes seems utopian to hope for alternative policies that would remove this threat. But in the past other causes, such as votes for women and the abolition of slavery, were dismissed as utopian and yet were successful in the end. Institutional momentum can allow a policy to continue for only so long in the face of mounting arguments and public concern. Suddenly a single event can tip the balance and trigger processes that lead rapidly to fundamental change. So it could be with the nuclear winter predictions and nuclear policy. Nuclear winter provides us with a challenge and an opportunity as well as a threat.

It will require an immense effort to halt and reverse the nuclear arms build-up. Even if the disarmament process starts soon, the effort will have to be sustained over a long period in order to reduce the nuclear stockpiles to below the nuclear threshold. Once this level is reached, new opportunities for further disarmament will arise. It is clearly a long term process. The important point is to get started before it is too late.

The preservation of humanity is our most fundamental responsibility. Its destruction would be the final crime. No generation, let alone a relatively small group of people, has the right to gamble with the lives of all future generations, nor should they be allowed to continue to do so. There is only one way to avoid this risk; to halt and reverse the nuclear arms race. Everybody has a fundamental interest in this. Can we all rise above immediate pressures and short-term interests for long enough to achieve it and remove the danger that threatens us? We believe that there is a real chance that we can.

Appendix 2.1

The Nuclear War Scenario

In this appendix the assumptions made in the nuclear war scenario (pp. 17–22) are described in more detail.

Table A2.11 summarizes which warheads were used and indicates what proportion this represents of the total number of warheads available on each type of weapon. The table is based on information on the present nuclear arsenals (as of winter 1984/85) from a range of sources. The principle references are listed in note 25, chapter 2. In some cases there is insufficient public information available, and so educated estimates have had to be made. We have made reasonable, if not conservative, assumptions throughout.

In deciding what proportion of the deliverable warheads would be used, we have taken into account the varying reliabilities of the different delivery vehicles and the fact that bombers are much more vulnerable to interception than missiles. It is normally assumed that 70–80 per cent of modern missiles would work reliably, whereas for older missiles the figure is more likely to be 50–60 per cent. We have kept within, and often far below, these margins. Many nuclear capable tactical or theatre aircraft would in fact be used for conventional attacks. This has also been taken into account.

The categories of targets that would probably be attacked are given in box 2.1 in chapter two. More accurate and reliable weapons would usually be used against blast resistant or high priority targets. Older, less accurate, or smaller-yield warheads

Table A2.11 The nuclear war scenario

Warhead type	Approximate % of total (deliverable) warheads used	Approximate % of total (deliverable) yield used	Number of warheads used	Total yield used (megatons)	Groundburst yield (megatons)
STRATEGIC					
USA:					
ICBM	67	56	1436	723.3	
SLBM	70	70	3740	257	
Air launched missiles	45	45	964	179	
Bombs	25	25	269	240.7	
US subtotal	60	46	6409	1400	808
USSR:					
ICBM	58	40	3260	2461	
SLBM	43	36	908	335	
Air-launched missiles	30	30	9	3.6	
Bombs	9	9	30	150	
USSR subtotal	52	43	4207	2789	1631

Table A2.11 continued
THEATRE/TACTICAL

USA:					
All other	<25	<40	~2159	~59	
Bombs	<25	<30	~1280	~696	
USSR					
Bombs/ASMs	<20	<25	~1151	~540	
All other	<25	<40	~2310	~344	
Subtotal	<25	<33	~6900	~1639	~921
UK	~31	~33	~146	~44	
France	~34	~41	~118	~44	
China	~25	~29	~87	~86	
Subtotal	~30	~33	~351	~174	~54
Total	~36	~40	~17867	~6002	~3414

Note: This table provides some details of the warheads used in the nuclear war scenario. The assumptions are discussed in the text of appendix 2.1.
Key: ~ — particularly approximate; < — less than.

would tend to be used against 'softer' targets. A few warheads might be detonated high in the atmosphere where they would generate a very intense pulse of radio waves (the Electromagnetic Pulse — EMP) which could damage or ruin electrical apparatus and communication facilities over vast areas. Nuclear warheads could also be used at sea — particularly low yield nuclear depth charges against submarines and missiles against ships. Such attacks are not taken into account in our scenario because they are not relevant to the nuclear winter effects and because the combined yield of warheads used in this way is likely to be relatively small.

Groundbursts would usually be used against relatively blast-resistant targets whereas airbursts would mostly be used against 'softer' targets such as radar stations, parked aircraft, or industrial centres. The altitude of detonation of airbursts would probably be chosen to maximize the area subjected to blast overpressures of more than 10 pounds per square inch (psi). Each warhead used in the scenario has been chosen to be a ground or air burst according to its capabilities and likely targets. The details are not given because of lack of space. However, the proportion (by yield) of assumed groundbursts is summarized in Table A2.11.

Attacks on Soviet missile fields are assumed to involve 630 Minuteman III (Mark 12A) warheads, 450 Minuteman III (Mark 12) warheads, 270 Minuteman II warheads and 400 air-launched cruise missiles. (These constitute the vast majority of the US warheads used in our scenario with a significant capability to destroy specially-hardened targets.) Soviet attacks on US missile fields are assumed to involve 624 SS18 (mod 2) and 1092 SS18 (mod 4) warheads. Altogether 3,466 warheads carrying a total yield of about 1,800 megatons are used against the 2,435 American and Soviet missile silos and over 100 of their associated launch-control centres. This is consistent with an assumption that each silo and launch-control centre was double targeted, but that some missiles did not work properly so that only about 70 per cent of them actually arrived.

A total of 17,867 warheads are used in the scenario, with a combined yield of 6,002 megatons. About 57 per cent of the yield is groundburst, of which about 80 per cent (by yield) comes from warheads with explosive powers of greater than or equal to half a megaton.

Appendix 2.2

Heat and Ignition caused by Nuclear Explosions

It is obvious from nuclear weapons tests and the experience of Hiroshima and Nagasaki that nuclear explosions can ignite fires over large areas. This appendix outlines how to estimate the amount of heat that would be received at a given distance from a nuclear explosion. It then explains and justifies the assumptions we have made about the areas over which the heat from a given warhead would ignite fires. Most of the appendix is based upon S. Glasstone and P. J. Dolan, *The effects of nuclear explosions*, (note 16, chapter 2).

A nuclear fireball radiates most of its thermal energy within a few seconds of the explosion. Low-yield weapons (in the kiloton range) emit nearly all of the thermal energy within one second. The energy received in a given area decreases with the distance from the explosion because the thermal radiation spreads as it travels outwards (the inverse square law), and also is absorbed and scattered by the molecules and aerosols in the atmosphere. As a rough approximation, it has been found that the amount of thermal radiation received a given distance away from an explosion is independent of visibility provided the atmosphere is at least moderately clear (a visibility of 10 miles or more). However, rain, fog, or dense industrial haze would significantly reduce the thermal energy received.

The thermal flux (Q calories per square centimeter) received at a distance D (kilometers) from a nuclear explosion is approximately given by the following equation:

$$Q = \frac{7.86 \times f \times W \times t}{D^2}$$

where f is the proportion of the explosive energy of the explosion that is manifested as thermal energy (for our purposes about 0.35 for an airburst and 0.18 for a groundburst); W is the yield of the warhead (in kilotons); and t is the transmittance, that is the fraction of the radiation (direct and scattered) that is transmitted out to the distance D. The equation is correct for a reasonably clear day (12 miles visibility). In combination with information given in Glasstone and Dolan, *The effects of nuclear explosions*, this formula enables us to estimate the thermal flux, Q, at any distance from a given explosion.

Clouds or snow cover could effect the relation between Q and D significantly, as they would reflect some of the thermal radiation. If an explosion occurred above a cloud layer, the thermal radiation received at the ground would be smaller than the above equation would indicate. On the other hand, clouds would reflect back towards the ground some of the heat from an explosion below them, typically increasing the value of Q at the ground by 50 per cent more than would expected in cloudless conditions. We make the assumption throughout that there is no cloud cover. This is conservative because the great majority of warheads used in the scenario would detonate beneath the clouds. Snow cover would also reflect some heat and increase the value of Q by 50 per cent, but conditions would not then be very suitable for the establishment of fires. Snow is also neglected in our calculations, since our main scenario is for a summer war.

The heat from a nuclear explosion can ignite imflammable materials far from the explosion. Table A2.21 shows the Q (thermal flux) values sufficient to ignite a selection of different materials. The information comes from nuclear weapons tests and laboratory experiments. Less thermal flux is required to ignite a given material from a low-yield explosion than from a high-yield weapon, because the radiation is received over a shorter time. The colour of the material is also important; the darker it is the more efficient it is at absorbing heat.

We define the fire ignition zone to be the area where the

Table A2.21 Thermal flux sufficient to ignite various materials

Material	Thermal radiation flux (Q) required for ignition (calories/sq cm)	
	35 kiloton yield (low)	1.4 megaton yield (high)
Newspaper	6	8
Deciduous leaves	4	6
Coarse grass (sedge)	6	9
Rayon rags (black)	9	14
3-ply Bristol board (dark)	16	20
Plywood (Douglas fir)	9	16
Roll roofing (smooth surface)	—	30

Note: The values of thermal flux given here are only accurate to about ±25 per cent. Data from S. Glasstone and P. Dolan, *The effects of nuclear weapons* (note 16, chapter 2).

thermal flux is greater than 12 calories per square centimeter. Fires would certainly be ignited outside this zone. In urban or industrial areas, blast damage caused by the explosion would start secondary fires out to areas subjected to overpressures to two pounds per square inch (2 psi) and further. For the typical range of warhead yields used in our scenario, places experiencing an overpressure of 2 psi would also be subjected to a thermal flux of between 5 and 9 calories per square centimeter and so some easily ignited materials would also be set on fire by the direct heat from the fireball at these places. Also, in many cases, fires would spread outwards from the ignition zone.

On the other hand, window glass would reduce the thermal radiation on materials inside rooms by about one-third, so that the flux might have to be 20 calories per square centimeter or more to ignite curtains and other fabrics inside buildings. On balance, in most circumstances areas subjected to more than 12 calories per square centimeter would be reasonably sure to have a sufficient density of fires to fully justify the term 'fire ignition zone'. The only exception to this would be grassland or forests in winter. In wet or snowy weather, woodland fires could not be expected to sustain themselves for long.

Using the equation quoted above, the distances at which a thermal flux of 12 calories per square centimeter would be received can be estimated for any yield of explosion. From this it is straightforward to calculate the areas of the ignition zones for each warhead, groundburst and airburst.

Appendix 2.3

Fire Ignition Areas in the Nuclear War Scenario

This appendix provides details of how the areas of urban, woodland, and grass or agricultural land which would fall within the ignition zones were estimated for the nuclear war scenario.

Appendix 2.1 described which warheads were assumed to be used in the scenario and whether they were groundbursts or airbursts. Combining this with the information from Glasstone and Dolan (note 16, chapter 2) summarized in appendix 2.2, it is straightforward to calculate the total ignition area that could result from the use of each type of warhead. If the warheads used in attacks on missile fields are omitted (they are considered separately), this area would be about 1,225,000 square kilometers. Since the total yield of the warheads used outside of the missile fields is about 4,200 megatons, this corresponds to an average ignition zone of just over 291 square kilometers per megaton. However overlap and double targeting is assumed to reduce the total ignition area by 10 per cent outside of Europe, to an area of about 260 square kilometers per megaton. In densely targeted Europe the overlap is assumed to be just over 20 per cent, making the average ignition zone of 230 square kilometers per megaton. This corresponds with the results of a study of the effects of a number of detailed nuclear attack scenarios on the UK (note 2, chapter 2). Naturally, overlap tends to be greater for heavier attacks. So a slightly larger factor could apply to the Germanies in our scenario. On the other hand, most areas of Europe would probably be less densely targeted than the UK, making an average 20 per cent reduction reasonable if not conservative.

Urban Fires

The urban area within ignition zones is estimated in two parts; large urban centres with more than 100,000 inhabitants, and smaller towns and villages.

Large Urban Centres

Table A2.31 shows the approximate number of large urban centres in the various regions of the world. A rough estimate is that they cover a total area of 1.5 million square kilometers and include 1.5 billion people. An urban centre includes both the metropolitan areas of the cities and the urban conglomerations and suburbs around them. Thus the average population density of 1,000 people per square kilometer is not unreasonable. In the USA, for example, the actual average could be less than this. In Europe and the USSR, the urban centres would tend to be more compact. In the metropolitan areas, and particularly in city centres, the population density would be higher.

We assume that about one-fifth of the total yield used in the nuclear war scenario is detonated over urban centres. About 88 per cent of this yield is assumed to be used in Europe, USA, or USSR. But cities in Canada, Cuba, Japan, China, the Middle East, Japan, Korea, Australia and elsewhere are almost bound to be affected, and so about 145 megatons is assumed to be used against these centres. Applying the different average ignition zone area per megaton for Europe and elsewhere, the total urban area within the ignition zones is estimated to be just over 300,000 square kilometers. Table A2.31 shows how this figure is built up from each region.

Assuming, crudely, that the average size of large urban centres is the same in each region considered, the urban area contained within ignition zones can be expressed as a percentage of the total area of large urban centres in each region. As table A2.31 shows, the estimated fire areas cover rather small percentages of the total areas. It should also be noted that by assuming that a high proportion (54 per cent) of the relevant

Table A2.31 Ignition zones and large urban centres

Region	Approximate number of urban centres with population greater than 100,000	Approximate yield used (megatons)	Approximate area within ignition zone (000s sq km)	Approximate percentage of total urban centre area within ignition zone
USA	280	215	56	30
USSR	270	208	54	30
Europe (not USSR)	580	667	153.5	40
North and South America (not USA)	300	23	6	3
Asia (not USSR)	610	100	26	6
Middle East/Africa	200	15	4	3
Elsewhere	20	6	1.5	14
Total	2260	1234	301	20

Note: The Table gives details of the approximate number of cities in various regions in the world and of how the estimate of the total urban ignition zone was arrived at.

yield is used in Europe, with its greater degree of overlap, the estimated urban area within ignition zones is smaller than it would otherwise have been.

In North and South America (excluding the USA), the ignition zones are assumed to include about 6,000 square kilometers of urban land. Since the combined area of Toronto, Montreal (in Canada) and Havana in Cuba is over 6,500 square kilometers this seems very conservative. Similarly, the 26,000 square kilometers of urban area in Asia is minimal; China, Japan and Korea, for example, all have many large cities and this ignition zone is only about five times larger than the metropolitan area of Shanghai.

Smaller Towns and Villages

The area ignited in lesser towns and villages is estimated in a different way. It is assumed that the ignition zones from the warheads are randomly located with respect to these populated areas. Taking an average population density outside of the cities, the number of people inside ignition zones can be estimated. The urban area corresponding to this number can then be roughly calculated by assuming that towns with less than 100,000 inhabitants have an average population density of 1,000 people per square kilometer.

Once attacks on missile fields and large urban centres are taken into account, the remaining yield is about 2,970 mega-tons, divided as shown in Table A2.32. The average population density outside the large urban centres is taken to be 100 people per square kilometer in Europe, 30 people per square kilometer in USA, USSR and the rest of the Americas, and 70 people per square kilometer in China, Japan and elsewhere. These are rather conservative estimates for Europe and Asia. In the USSR and America, the average population density is actually 10–15 people per square kilometer, but the warheads would tend to be concentrated on areas with relatively high population densities within this region, and so the assumption is reasonable.

This crude method leads to an estimate that some 39 million people outside of the large urban centres would be within the ignition zones, corresponding to an urban area of over 39,000 square kilometers.

Table A2.32 Ignition zones and towns and villages

Region	Yield used outside outside large urban centres or missile fields (mts)	Approximate total ignition area (000s sq km)	Assumed population density (people/sq km)	Approximate number of people inside zone (millions)	Approximate urban area (000s sq km)
Europe	893	206	100	21	21
USA/USSR/South and North America	1835	477	30	14	14
Elsewhere	240	62	70	4	4
Total	2968	—	—	39	39

Note: This table shows how we estimated the number of people outside large urban centres who would be within the ignition zones. It also gives the approximate urban area in towns and villages that this represents.

Wildfires

The wildfires from the attack woud be generated by explosions over missile fields and other targets outside of the urban areas. These will be considered separately.

Missile fields

The warheads used in attacks on missile fields are detailed in appendix 2.1. The attacks are so heavy that every part of each missile field would be subjected to intense heat from at least one explosion, and nearly always more than one. It is very likely that nearly all the wood, grass and other fuels in these areas would be consumed by fire.

   The missile fields in the USA are mostly (roughly 80 per cent) in grass or agricultural land. It is assumed that only 3,000 square kilometers (less than three per cent) of the total area of the US missile fields is wooded. In contrast, about half of the missile fields in the Soviet Union are in forested regions. To be conservative, we assume that only one-third of the area actually in and around the missile fields is forested. A further 47 per cent is taken to be grass or agricultural land. The resulting estimated ignition areas are given in Table A2.33.

Table A2.33 The estimated area of wildfires ignited by the nuclear war scenario

| Type | Ignition area (000s sq km) | | | |
| | Missile fields | | Outside missile fields | Total |
	USA	USSR	Europe	Elsewhere	
Forest	3	50	74	209	⁀ 336
Grass/agricultural land	88	70	74	209	~440
Other	19	30	37	104	190

Note: The table shows the area of forest and grass or agricultural land that would be within the ignition area caused by nuclear attacks on missile fields and elsewhere.

Outside the missile fields

In the nuclear war scenario about 2,970 megatons are used outside of missile fields and large urban centres. Much of this would explode over woodland. About 37 per cent of the relevant regions are forested, with grass and agricultural land covering a similar proportion.

The forested area within the ignition zones is taken to be 37 per cent of the total ignition zone outside of large urban areas and missile fields. The actual estimates are that 283,000 square kilometers of forest would be inside ignition zones. A similar area of grass and agricultural land and about 141,000 square kilometers of scrub and other land is also assumed to be covered by the ignition zones.

Summary

Altogether, an estimated 336,000 square kilometers of forest, 441,000 square kilometers of grass or agricultural land, and about 340,000 square kilometers of urban land would be contained within the ignition zones caused by our nuclear war scenario.

Appendix 3.1

Quantity and Properties of Smoke

Smoke continually changes; it is first formed as particles between 0.01 and 0.1 micron across, but these coagulate into larger clusters, rapidly at first and then more slowly. It is also affected by water in the atmosphere, for example in passing through clouds, but the blackest carbon smoke is less affected, because it repels water. Its optical properties are probably best determined by observation, because the usual microscopic theory is based on the assumption that the smoke clusters are spherical, which is very far from the case.

Smoke absorbs and scatters light, and both processes are important. The 'extinction' includes both absorption and scattering, and is measured in square meters per gram: A 1 meter layer of air containing 1 gram per cubic meter of smoke with extinction coefficient 1 square meter per gram reduces the intensity of a beam of light passing through it perpendicularly by a factor $e = 2.7$. Such a layer is said to have an optical depth of 1. Doubling the extinction coefficient, the thickness or the density reduces the intensity by the square, a factor of about 8, according to the exponential extinction law, and has optical depth 2.

In practice sunlight does not pass through smoke clouds perpendicularly, and some reaches the ground after being scattered inside the smoke layer, so the proportion of sunlight reaching the ground is not given exactly by the extinction coefficient. The relation between them is given approximately for smoke and dust with sunlight at zenith angle of 60 degrees in

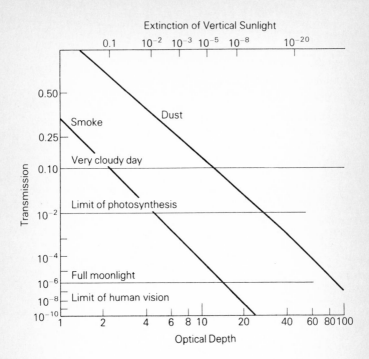

Figure A3.11. Fraction of incident solar radiation reaching the surface of the Earth as a function of the extinction optical depth for smoke and dust, assuming 60 degree solar zenith angle

Note: This figure allows one to translate between the extinction optical depth (reduction in the light coming directly from the sun if it were directly overhead) and the amount of sunlight getting to the ground when the sun is at an angle. These are not the same. For example for smoke an extinction optical depth of about fifteen would correspond to a full moonlit night, whereas for dust it would correspond to a very cloudy day. This is because of the comparatively dark colour of smoke.

figure A3.11, based on a graph in the NRC report drawn from the calculations of Pollack et al., 'Environmental effects of an impact-generated dust-cloud', *Science* 219, 287–9 (1983).

The NRC report (note 5, chapter 1) provides estimates of quantities of smoke and its optical properties, which are reproduced in table A3.11 for reference purposes. The total

Table A3.11 Fire and smoke parameters in the NRC nuclear war analysis

	Baseline	Excursions[a]
Urban fire smoke emission, Tg	150	20–450
Forest fire smoke emission, Tg	30	0–200
Total smoke emission, Tg	180	20–650
Tropospheric injection, Tg/km	20 (0–9 km)	1.5–53 (0–12 km)
Stratospheric injection, Tg/km	0	1 (12–20 km)
Urban fire area, km^2	250,000	125,–375,000
Urban fuel consumption, g/cm^2	3.0	1.5–3.0
Urban smoke emission factor, [b] g/g	0.02	0.01–0.04
Urban fire duration, days	≤1	—
Forest fire area, km^2	250,000	0–1,000,000
Forest fuel consumption, g/cm^2	0.4	0.4
Forest smoke emission factor, g/g	0.03	0.02–0.05
Forest fire duration, weeks	≤1	—
Smoke composition (by mass)	20% graphitic carbon, 80% oils	5–50% graphitic carbon
Smoke refractive index (visible)[c]	1.55–0.10 i	1.5–0.02 i to 1.7–0.30 i
Smoke particle number median size, μm	0.10	0.05–0.5
Smoke particle log normal width, γ	2.0	2.0
Smoke specific extinction (visible),[c] m^2/g	5.5	2.0–9.0
Smoke specific absorption (visible),[c] m^2/g	2.0	1.0–6.0
Smoke specific absorption (infrared), m^2/g	0.5	0.2–5.0

Notes: a Some values are given only to illustrate the range that is plausible.
b Average value after 50 per cent prompt scavenging in the convective fire columns.
c At a nominal wavelength of 550 nm.

amount of smoke is measured in Tg, a unit equal to a million tonnes. The 150 Tg of the first row is equivalent to the 0.6 micron of smoke over the hemisphere given in box 3.1.

Appendix 3.2

Height of Mushroom Clouds

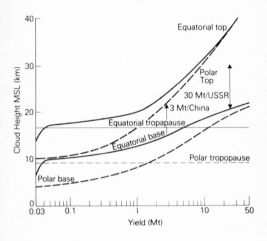

Figure A3.21. Height of mushroom clouds as function of yield
of nuclear explosion

The graph is adapted from K. R. Peterson, 'An empirical
model for estimating world-wide deposition from atmospheric
nuclear detonations', *Health Phys.* 18, 357–8 (1970). It shows
the dependence of equilibrium cloud height on the yield of the
nuclear explosion, with an indication of dependence on
latitude.

Appendix 3.3

Height of Smoke Plumes

The formula of box 3.2 is used here to obtain smoke plume heights for two examples: a large fast-burning city fire, and a smaller slow-burning fire. First we have to find the heat produced by the fire; this depends on the fire area A, the density of combustible material that is burnt D and the half-burning time t, which is explained below.[a] The values are given in the following table.

Quantity	Symbol	Value Larger	Smaller	Units
Fire area	A	250	50	sq km
Average density of combustibles burned	D	30	20	kg/sq m
Time of half-burning[a]	t	2	8	hours

a The power of a fire changes all the time. Here we calculate the smoke plume produced during a period of fiercest burning, during which half of the total heat is produced. This part of the plume might contain about half of the smoke emitted by the fire. The rest of the smoke is emitted when the fire is burning less fiercely, so it does not go so high. It will probably occupy a region between ground level and the calculated base of the smoke plume.

The average heat q produced by burning wood and similar materials is about 10^7 joules per kilogram, so the total amount of heat produced by the fires is

$$Q = q \times A \times D$$

Half of this heat is produced during the period t of fiercest burning, so the power of the fire, which is the rate at which it produces heat, is given by

$$w = \frac{Q}{(2t)}/(2t) = \frac{q \times A \times D}{(2t)}$$

where the time is measured in seconds and the power in joules. On using the formula of box 3.2, the following values of the power and the height of the smoke plume are obtained:

		Larger	*Smaller*	*Units*
Power of fire	w	10	0.35	10^6 MW
Top[b]		14	6	km
Base		9	3.5	km

b If the formula gives either of the heights in the stratosphere, then the actual height is between the tropopause and the formula height.

The height of the plume could be decreased by strong winds, temperature inversion, radiative cooling at night or outward movement of the air surrounding the fire. It could be increased by high ambient humidity, marginal stability (as before thunderstorms), heating by the Sun or by inward movement of the surrounding air. Examples are given in the NRC report (note 5, chapter 1).

Appendix 4.1

Transfer of Smoke to the Southern Hemisphere

The NCAR model (note 8, chapter 4) includes the changes in the circulation of the atmosphere produced by a uniform smoke distribution in northern midlatitudes, which strongly infuences the vertical movement of the air. The change is sketched in figure 4.11, during the 16–20 days following an April war. Note how the air in the northern troposphere moves into the stratosphere and then southward into the Southern Hemisphere. This would carry smoke with it, but this transport of smoke was not included in the NCAR model explicitly.

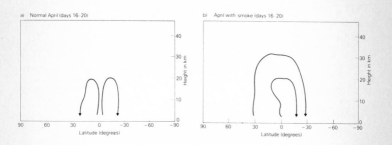

Figure A4.11. Change in atmospheric circulation caused by an April war (simplified)

Note: After Covey et al. (note 8, chapter 4).

Appendix 4.2

Intermediate Fallout

The TTAPS group (see note 2, chapter 1) suggest that the average whole-body dose of gamma-rays in the mid-latitudes of the Northern Hemisphere might be 50 rads. But radioactivity would be heavily concentrated in areas with rain or snow, with dosages that would sometimes be ten times higher, leaving arid regions with little radioactivity. So rain essential for plant life would be accompanied by increased radioactivity.

Appendix 6.1

Low Temperature Damage to Plants

Plants can be divided, very broadly, into three groups with respect to their tolerance of cold. There are:

i *Chilling-sensitive species*. These are damaged if the temperature falls to somewhere between 0 and 15°C (depending on the species). They can never tolerate prolonged frost and include large numbers of tropical species and also temperate crops such as tomatoes, cucumbers and some varieties of maize.

ii *Chilling-resistant species able to develop limited resistance to freezing temperatures*. These species are not killed unless temperatures fall below freezing and what happens then depends on whether the plants are 'prepared' — hardened against cold. If they are, they can tolerate prolonged frost at temperatures ranging from 0 to about −15°C. Most of the non-woody (herbaceous) plants in the temperate zone, including major cereal crops such as wheat and barley, belong to this group.

iii *Extremely freezing-resistant species*. These species resemble group ii except that, when fully cold hardened, they can tolerate prolonged periods of very low temperatures in the range of −50 to −70°C (or even lower). Most native trees and shrubs in the temperate and polar latitudes belong to this group.

In the context of a nuclear winter, it is obviously critical to know what conditions are necessary to induce cold hardening. Three important points are:

a Cold hardening is a *gradual* process that usually requires two to five weeks at cool but above-freezing temperatures before it is well established. In group iii species, decreasing temperatures coupled with decreasing day length in autumn induce freezing resistance before the onset of winter — this is why gardeners harden off their seedlings so carefully in spring. Cold hardening involves quite complex changes to cells and this is why so much time is required and a lot of energy (stored food reserves) is used for the hardening process.

b Plants which are diseased or damaged (by ionizing radiation, for example) do not harden properly to cold.

c Cold hardening is *reversible* and quite easily lost. Most trees, for example, lose their winter hardiness by the end of March. And some varieties of potato de-harden after only one or two days at 10–20°C. It follows that rapid fluctuations in temperature to below freezing and back again are among the most stressful conditions for plants.

Two other topics need to be considered here. First, the time factor and how duration of exposure to cold affects the level of injury; and second, how cold sensitivity varies at different stages of the life cycle and between different plant organs (the development/organ factor).

The Time Factor

All plants *eventually* succumb to low temperatures. To give an extreme example, 100 days of sub-zero temperature would be expected to destroy virtually all temperate plants if occurring during spring or summer. These conditions are predicted for the very 'severe' nuclear winter scenario (chapter 5). Table A6.11 illustrates how the time factor can operate with chilling sensitive plants exposed to chilling temperatures: the most sensitive species showed signs of injury within 18 hours and were dead within 5 days, whereas the most resistant species were injured only after 20 days and dead by 30–35 days.

Other chilling sensitive species are even more sensitive than this. When shoots of a tradescantia (*Tradescantia zebrina*) and a fittonia (*Fittonia argyroneura*), both common as houseplants, are cooled to 6°C, leaves are damaged and wilt within one to two *minutes*. And when leaves of the coffee tree are cooled to 3°C, leaf damage (discoloration) occurs in six hours. Cucumber leaves can survive for 7 days at 10°C, 3 days at 8°C but for only a few hours at 5°C before showing signs of injury. In general, the longer a plant is exposed to stressful cold temperatures, the more likely it is to be damaged and eventually to die.

Table A6.11 The time required for chilling damage in tropical species

Species	Time for first injury to appear	Time for complete killing (days)
Episcia (*Episcia bicolor*)	18 hours	5
Eranthemum (*Eranthemum tricolor*)	48 hours	4–5
Eranthemum (*Eranthemum couperi*)	3–5 days	10
Iresine (*Iresine acuminata*)	8 days	19
Uhdea (*Uhdea bipinnatifida*)	11 days	16
Blue eranthemum (*Eranthemum nervosum*)	20 days	30–35

Note: a) Whole plants were exposed continuously to 1.4–3.7°C in rather dim, diffuse light.

b) All these plants are rainforest species, commonly cultivated in tropical gardens and as houseplants. Cultivation instructions for indoor episcias and eranthemums advise 'moist, shady conditions and *minimum* temperatures of 16°C (61°F) winter and summer'.

c) The table is based on Molisch, 1897 and is taken from J. Levitt, *Responses of plants to environmental stresses. I. Chilling, freezing and high temperature stresses*, 2nd edn (Academic Press, New York: 1980).

The Development/Organ Factor

Even from the few examples given it must be obvious that different species within groups i to iii differ in their sensitivity to cold. To complicate matters further, different stages in the development of a plant and different organs within a plant can differ in cold sensitivity. As a rough guide:

a Any stage or organ that is dormant (seeds, buds or tubers for instance) is likely to show quite high resistance to cold.

b Woody tissues are usually more resistant than soft tissues at all times of year and develop greater cold resistance in winter.

c Any stages or organs where there is active, rapid growth are likely to be especially sensitive to low temperatures: germinating seeds, young seedlings, and new leaves or sprouts, for example.

d The formation of flowers, especially pollen development, and the early stages of seed and fruit development are often highly sensitive to cold.

Chilling or freezing at these critical developmental stages can cause sterility or prevent seed or fruit set. We give particular examples of this problem, which can be severe for some crops on pp. 102–5.

Appendix 6.2

Computer Simulations of Ecosystem Recovery from Reductions by Light or Temperature

This appendix summarizes information from Harwell, *The human and environmental consequences of nuclear war* (note 10, chapter 6).

Forest

The simulation exercise was carried out for a mixed conifer and hardwood forest, typical of Eastern Tennessee. The exercise ignored the extreme conditions in the first few months after a nuclear war, and assumed that all trees had remained alive. It also assumed normal conditions of light and rainfall and a reduction in the average annual temperature of either 3, 6 or 9°C for a period of 5 years (from 1–6 years after a nuclear war). It demonstrated that the effects shown in figure 6.21 and summarized below would be probable.

i For a 3°C reduction, the mass of living trees (biomass) is predicted to fall by 25 per cent in five years, recovering after 30–40 years.

ii For a 6°C reduction, biomass would fall by 80 per cent in five years and would be only about 50 per cent of normal 50 years later.

iii For a 9°C reduction, biomass would fall by 90 per cent in five years and still be only one third of normal 50 years later.

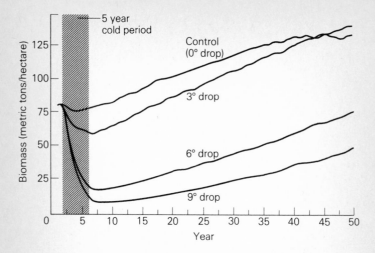

Other simulations were carried out to estimate the effects of temperature reduction on species composition of the forests. Compared with the control, 20 years after the 3°C reduction, one species had disappeared; after the 6 or 9°C reduction, five species had disappeared and three were more plentiful.

Grassland

The simulation was carried out for a prairie grassland ecosystem typical of Colorado, US. The same assumptions were made as for the forest exercise, but the effets of a reduction in light intensity were also calcualted.

The results of this simulation are shown in table A6.21 and summarized below.

i A reduction of 3°C in average temperature or 25 per cent in light intensity over 5 years had similar, small effects on plant growth. The ecosystem had almost completely recovered in two years.

ii Temperature reductions of 6 or 9°C caused progressively greater inhibition of plant growth, with no evidence of recovery after two years. There was some recovery two years after reductions in light intensity of 50 or 75 per cent.

Table A6.21 Computer simulation of the effects on plant growth (net primary production) of a five year period of temperature reduction or of reduction in light intensity for a grassland ecosystem in the US

Year	Net primary production (% of control)						
	Temperature reduction				Insolation reduction		
	0 (control)	3°C	6°C	9°C	0 (control)	25%	50%	75%
1	100	91	72	58	100	89	76	61
2	100	87	67	49	100	96	89	82

Note: Based on Harwell, *The human and environmental consequences of nuclear war* (note 10, chapter 6).
Figure A6.21 and table A6.21 © Professor Mark Harwell.

Notes and References

Superscript numbers in the notes refer readers to the first full reference to each title, with chapter number first, then the note number.

1. Introduction

1. P. J. Crutzen and J. W. Birks, 'The atmosphere after a nuclear war: twilight at noon', *Ambio* 11, 114–125 (1982); reprinted in J. Peterson (ed.), 'Nuclear war: the aftermath' (Special *Ambio* Publication), (Pergamon, Oxford: 1983).
2. R. P. Turco, O. B. Toon, T. P. Ackerman, J. B. Pollack and C. Sagan (TTAPS), 'Nuclear winter: global consequences of multiple nuclear explosions', *Science* 222, 1283–1292 (1983); reprinted as appendix to P. R. Ehrlich, C. Sagan, D. Kennedy and W. O. Roberts, 'The cold and the dark: the world after nuclear war (The Conference on the Long-term World-wide Biological Consequences of Nuclear War)' (Sidgwick and Jackson, London: 1984); reprinted in modified form in TTAPS, *Scientific American* 251, 23–33 (1984). More detail of the computer modelling is given in TTAPS 'Global atmospheric consequences of nuclear war' (Preprint, R & D Associates, Marina del Rey, California 94035, USA).
3. P. R. Ehrlich and 19 other authors, 'Long-term biological consequences of nuclear war', *Science* 1293–1300 (1983); reprinted as appendix to 'The cold and the dark'.[1/2]
4. 'The cold and the dark'.[1/2]

5. National Research Council of the US Academy of Sciences, Committee on the Atmospheric Effects of Nuclear Explosions, 'The effects on the atmosphere of a major nuclear exchange' (National Academy Press, Washington, DC: 1985).

6. The International Council of Scientific Unions is the principal co-ordinating body of the National Academies and Scientific Societies of the World. SCOPE is their Scientific Committee on Problems of the Environment, which in 1983 set up the ENUWAR steering committee on the Environmental Consequences of Nuclear War, chaired by Sir Frederick Warner, with services provided by the University of Essex, England.

7. The Royal Society of Canada, 'Nuclear winter and associated effects' (Report of the Committee on the Environmental Consequences of Nuclear War, Royal Society of Canada, Ottawa: 31 January 1985).

2. Fires and the Scale of Nuclear War

1. British Medical Association, *The medical effects of nuclear war* (J. Wiley & Sons, Chichester: 1983), p. 41. A detailed study of the effects of nuclear attack on London can be found in O. Greene, B. Rubin, N. Turok, P. Webber, G. Wilkinson, *London after the bomb* (Oxford University Press, Oxford: 1982).

2. S. Openshaw, P. Steadman and O. Greene, *Doomsday: Britain after nuclear attack* (Basil Blackwell, Oxford: 1983), p. 140.

3. For estimates at the upper end of the range see: J. Peterson and D. Hinrichsen (eds), *Nuclear war: the aftermath* (Pergamon, Oxford: 1982), p. 162; J. Rotblat, *Nuclear radiation in warfare*, (Taylor & Francis, London: 1981); and the World Health Organisation 'The effects of nuclear war on health and health services (Report of the International Committee of experts in medical sciences and public health, World Health Organization, Geneva, Switzerland: 1984). Estimates at the lower end are given in studies by US government agencies such as: US Arms Control and

Disarmament Agency (ACDA), *The effects of nuclear war*, April 1979; Defense Civil Preparedness Agency, US Department of Defense, *DCPA attack environment manual* (Publication CPG2-1A, 9 vols, June 1973; vol. 4 revised June 1977). See also Office of Technology Assessment, *The effects of nuclear war* (Croom Helm, London: 1982), appendix D.

4. H. Hjort, 'The impact on global food supplies'; E. Bondietti, 'Effects on agriculture'; Y. Laulan, 'Economic consequences; back to the Dark Ages'; all in J. Peterson and D. Hinrichsen (eds), *Nuclear war: the aftermath*.[2/3]

5. D. Ball, 'US Strategic forces: how would they be used?', *International Security* 7/3 (1982/83), pp. 31–60; D. Ball, *Targeting for strategic deterrence* (Adelphi paper no. 185, International Institute of Strategic Studies, London: 1983); P. Rogers and W. Arkin, *Bulletin of the Atomic Scientists* (April 1983) p. 9.

6. This is briefly reviewed, for example, in S. Openshaw, P. Steadman and O. Greene, *Doomsday: Britain after nuclear attack*, chapter 2,[2/2] and B. Lambeth and K. Lewis 'Economic targeting in modern warfare', *Rand Papers, P-6735* (Rand Corporation, Santa Monica: July 1982) and the references contained in these texts.

7. Good references include P. Bracken, *The command and control of nuclear forces* (Yale University Press, New Haven/London: 1983); I. Clark, *Limited nuclear war* (Martin Robinson, Oxford: 1982); D. Ball, *Can nuclear war be controlled?* (Adelphi paper no 169, International Institute of Strategic Studies, London: 1981).

8. 'We know that what might start as a supposedly controlled, limited strike could well, in my view very likely, escalate to a full-scale nuclear war.'
H. Brown, *The flexibility of our plans: strategic nuclear policy*, speech delivered at the Convocation Ceremonies for the 97th Naval War College Class, Newport, Rhode Island, August 20 1980. President Reagan made a similar statement about limiting Nuclear War to Europe in 1981 (*Atlantic News*, 23 October 1981).

9. For the USA, see for example: D. Ball, *Targeting for strategic deterrence*.[2/5] See also US Congress, Senate, Committee on Foreign Relations, *Nuclear war strategy* (Top secret hearing held on September 16 1980; sanitized and

printed on 18 February 1981) for US 'launch under attack' and 'launch on warning' plans in the event of 'unequivocal warning' of Soviet attack. For the USSR see note 6, chapter 2.

10. US Congress, Senate, Committee on Armed Services, *Department of Defense Authorisation for Appropriation for Fiscal Year 1981* (US Government Printing Office, Washington DC: 1980), part 5, p. 2721. See also D. Ball, *US strategic forces; how would they be used?*[2/5]

11. V. Ye. Savkin, 'Basic Principles of operational art and tactics (A Soviet view)', *Soviet Military Thought* (US Air Force, 1974).

12. D. Rumsfeld, *Annual Defense Report, Fiscal Year 1977* (US Government Printing Office, Washington DC: 1976), quoted in B. Lambeth and K. Lewis, *Economic targeting in modern warfare.*[2/6]

13. The Stackpole Company, *Air Force bases: a directory of US Air Force installations*, (The Military Service Publishing Co., Harrisburg Pa: 1965); 'Is the South safe?', *South* (Jan. 1984), p. 15; 'Asia; theatre of nuclear war', *South* (Nov. 1983), pp. 9–13.

14. See, for example, P. Rogers, *Guide to nuclear weapons, 1984–85* (University of Bradford, Bradford: 1984).

15. P. Crutzen and J. Birks, 'The atmosphere after a nuclear war: twilight at noon'.[1/1] Crutzen and Birks estimate that it would take a total of only four megatons of nuclear weapons to uncap all forty or fifty oil and gas wells in the North Sea (p. 80).

16. The most authoritative reference on nuclear explosions and their effects is S. Glasstone and P. Dolan, *The effects of nuclear weapons* (US Department of Defense and US Energy Research and Development Administration), (US Government Printing Office, Washington DC: 1977). Unless otherwise stated, we have used this reference throughout for information on nuclear explosions and their direct effects.

17. National Research Council, 'The effects on the atmosphere of a major nuclear exchange', pp. 46–7.[1/5] Information also from the SCOPE–ENUWAR Fire Workshop held at the Royal Society, London, 16–18 April 1984.

18. National Research Council, p. 48;[1/5] SCOPE-ENUWAR.[1/6]

19. National Research Council, p. 46;[1/5] SCOPE-ENUWAR;[1/6] J. Backovsky, R. Alger, S. Martin, *Predicting Secondary Fires* (preprint, Stanford Research Institute International: 1984).

20. British Medical Association, *The medical effects of nuclear war*, p. 41.[2/1].

21. R. Huschke, *The simultaneous flammability of wildlands and fuels in the United States*, RM-5073-TAB (Rand Corporation, Santa Monica: 1966); National Research Council, p. 50.[1/5] See also M. Harwell, *Nuclear winter: the human and environmental consequences of nuclear war* (Springer-Verlag, New York: 1984), pp. 56–62.

22. D. Larson, R. Small, *Analysis of the large urban fire environment* (PSR report 1210, Pacific Sierra Research Corporation, Santa Monica, California: 1982).

23. R. Turco, O. Toon, T. Ackerman, J. Pollack, C. Sagan (TTAPS), 'Nuclear winter: global consequences of multiple nuclear explosions'.[1/2]

24 National Research Council, pp. 22–6.[1/5] For large yield warheads, values at the lower end of the range would apply.

25. Estimated from a number of sources, including: International Institute of Strategic Studies, *The Military Balance* (IISS, London: 1984); Stockholm International Peace Research Institute, *World armaments and disarmament, SIPRI yearbook 1984* (Taylor & Francis, London: 1984); David Fairhall, *Guardian* 24 January 1985; P. Rogers, *Guide to nuclear weapons, 1984–85*;[2/14] T. Cochran, W. Arkin, M. Hoenig, *Nuclear weapons databook* (Ballinger, Cambridge, Mass.: 1984); P. Bracken, *The command and control of nuclear forces*.[2/7]

26. S. Openshaw, P. Steadman and O. Greene, *Doomsday: Britain after nuclear attack*.[2/2]

27. The National Research Council[1/5] take a global value of 250 square kilometers per megaton for ignition zones in cities and between 250 and 500 square kilometers per megaton for wildfires. TTAPS[1/2] estimates were the same as those of the NRC, except that they took the upper estimate for wildfires. P. Crutzen and I. Galbally ('Atmospheric conditions after a nuclear war', paper presented at the study week *Chemical events and their impact on the environment*, 5–11 November 1983, at the Pontifical Academy of Sciences, The Vatican) assume an average of 375 square

kilometers per megaton for urban fires.

28. D. Ball, *Can nuclear war be controlled?* p. 30.[2/7]

29. Data compiled from the *1977 demographic yearbook (1980), county and city data book, (1977);* and many other sources. Quoted in notes prepared by TTAPS for a report now available as *Global atmospheric consequences of nuclear war* (Interim report, R & D Associates, Marina del Rey, Calif.: 1984). See also NRC, 'The effects on the atmosphere of a major nuclear exchange', p. 51.[1/5]

30. E. Ishikawa, D. L. Swain (trans), *Hiroshima and Nagasaki: the physical, medical, and social effects of the atomic bombings* (Hutchinson, London: 1981), p. 55, for Hiroshima. For Dresden; see city council records.

31. NRC, 'The effects on the atmosphere of a major nuclear exchange', p. 53.[1/5]

32. P. Crutzen and J. Birks, *The atmosphere after a nuclear war: twilight at noon;*[1/1] I. Galbally, P. Crutzen and H. Rodhe, in M. Denborough (ed.), *Australia and nuclear war* (Croom Helm, London: 1983).

33. For groundburst yields of between 0.5 and 1 megaton, about 300,000 tonnes of dust per megaton would be sent into the atmosphere: NRC, 'The effects on the atmosphere of a major nuclear exchange', chapter 4.[1/5]

34. TTAPS and NRC assume 250,000 square kilometers of urban fires. P. Crutzen and I. Galbally,[1/2] estimate 500,000 square kilometers.

35. R. Small and B. Bush, *Wildland fires from a nuclear exchange* (Submitted to science, Pacific-Sierra Research Co.: 1984) estimate only 70,000 square kilometers of forest fires for a 4,000 megaton war (corresponding to about 100,000 square kilometeres for a 6,000 megaton exchange). P. Crutzen and J. Birks,[1/1] estimated a fire area in forests of one million square kilometers; TTAPS estimated 500,000 square kilometers; P. Crutzen, I. Galbally and C. Bruhl, 'Atmospheric effects from post nuclear fires', *Climatic change* (forthcoming, 1985), estimated 200,000 to 1,000,000 square kilometers; and the NRC[1/5] estimated 250,000 square kilometers of wildfires in forests.

36. See G. Kemp, 'Nuclear forces for medium powers', *Adelphi papers* 106 and 107 (IISS, London: 1974) for further discussion of the potential effects of French and British nuclear forces.

3. Fires, Smoke and the Atmosphere

1. R. E. Huschke, *The simultaneous flammability of wildlands and fuels in the United States.*[2/21]
2. After E. Ishikawa and D. L. Swain (trans), *Hiroshima and Nagasaki.*[2/30]
3. National Research Council Report 1985.[1/5] The amount of sunlight was obtained from the table and graph reproduced in our appendix 3.1, using 5.5 square meters per gram for the extinction coefficient as in the table and then using the figure for the transmission.
4. TTAPS, 'The cold and the dark'.[1/2]
5. P. J. Crutzen, I. E. Galbally and C. Bruehl, 'Atmospheric effects from postnuclear fires', *Climatic Change* 6, 323–364 (1984).
6. P. C. Manins, 'Cloud heights and stratospheric injections resulting from a thermonuclear war', submitted to *Atmosphere and Environment*. See also G. A. Briggs in *Lectures on air pollution and environmental impact analysis* (American Meteorological Society, Boston, Mass., USA: 1975) , pp. 59–111.
Recent computer models of large fires allow a more thorough study, and experiments have been a valuable check on their validity: they suggest that the formula is a good rough guide to the plume height, subject to the variations listed at the end of appendix 3.3. See R. D. Small, D. A. Larson and H. L. Brode, 'Asymptotically large fire areas', *Journal of Heat Transfer* 106, 318–324 (1984); R. D. Fletter, F. E. Fendell, L. M. Cohen, N. Gat and A. B. White, 'Laboratory facility for wind-aided firespread along a fuel matrix', *Combustion and Flame* 57, 289–311 (1984); the NRC Report,[1/5] and references in all these publications.

4. War on the Atmosphere

1. C. D. Smith, 'The widespread smoke layer from the Canadian forest fires during late September 1950', *Monthly Weather Review* 78, 180–184 (1950).
2. A. Robock and C. Moss, 'The Mount St Helen's volcanic

eruption of 18 May 1980: large short-term surface temperature effects', *Science* 216, 628–630 (1982).

3. S. L. Thompson, V. V. Aleksandrov, G. L. Stenchikov, S. H. Schneider, C. Covey and R. M. Chervin, 'Global climatic consequences of nuclear war: simulations with three-dimensional models', *Ambio* 13, 236–243 (1984).

4. H. Lamb, 'Climate: past present and future, Vol. 1' (Methuen, London: 1972); P. M. Kelly and C. B. Sear, 'Climatic impact of explosive volcanic eruptions', *Nature* 311, 740–743 (1984).

5. A. Robock, 'Snow and ice feedbacks prolong effects of nuclear winter', *Nature* 310, 667–670 (1984).

6. NRC report,[1/5] pages 39, 66–68, 77–80, 85–86, 104, 131. Although scavenging in the smoke plume was observed to be small at Hiroshima and for the computer models of fires, the Report conservatively assumes that of the 4% by mass of smoke produced by city combustibles, only 2% remains after passing through the smoke plume.

7. M. C. MacCracken, 'Nuclear war: preliminary estimates of the climatic effects of a nuclear exchange', paper presented at the third session of the International Seminar on Nuclear War, Sicily, 19–23 August 1983; M. C. MacCracken and J. Walton, 'The effects of interactive transport and scavenging of smoke on the calculated temperature change resulting from large amounts of smoke', ibid., fourth session, 1984.

8. C. Covey, S. H. Schneider and S. L. Thompson, 'Global atmospheric effects of massive smoke injections from a nuclear war: results from general circulation model simulations', *Nature* 308, 21–25 (1984). This is the 'NCAR paper'.

9. V. V. Aleksandrov and G. L. Stenchikov, *On the modelling of the climatic consequences of the nuclear war* (Proceedings on Applied Mathematics of the USSR Academy of Sciences Computing Centre, Moscow: 1983).

10. Unpublished circular to participants in the ENUWAR inquiry.[1/6]

5. Uncertainties and Risks

1. R. D. Mountain and G. W. Mulholland 'Stochastic dynamics simulation of particle aggregation', in *Kinetics of aggregation*

and gelation: Proceedings of the international topical conference on kinetics of aggregation and gelation 2–4 April 1984, Athens, Georgia, USA, F. Family and D. P. Landau (eds) (North-Holland, Amsterdam: 1984), pp. 83–6.

6. War on the Living

1. See TTAPS, 1983.[1/2]
2. After H. van Keulen, W. Lowerse, L. Sibma and M. Alberda. 'Crop simulation ad experimental evaluation — a case study', in *Photosynthesis and productivity in different environments*, ed. J. P. Cooper (Cambridge University Press, Cambridge: 1975), pp. 623–43.
3. After R. E. Redman, *Photosynthesis, plant respiration, and soil respiration measured with controlled environment chambers in the field*. Canadian Committee, IBP Technical Report 49 (University of Saskatchewan, Saskatoon, Canada 1974).
4. H. Bauer, W. Larcher and R. B. Walker, 'Influences of temperature stress on CO_2-gas exchange', in *Photosynthesis and productivity in different environments*, pp. 557–186.[6/2]
5. After W. Larcher and H. Bauer 'Ecological significance of resistance to low temperature' in *Encyclopedia of plant physiology vol.12A: physiological plant ecology I* (Springer-Verlag, Berlin, Heidelberg, New York: 1981), pp. 403–437.
6. F. C. Sweeney and J. M. Hopkinson, 'Vegetative growth of nineteen tropical and sub-tropical pasture grasses and legumes in relation to temperature', *Tropical Grassland* 9, 209, (1975).
7. Data from A. D. Taylor and J. A. Rowley, 'Plants under climatic stress I: Low temperature, high light effects on photosynthesis', *Plant Physiology* 47, 713–18 (1971).
8. From L. R. Humphries, *Environmental adaptation of tropical pasture plants* (Macmillan, London and Basingstoke: 1981). Figure 6.4 was based on Sweeney and Hopkinson [6/6] and is © The Tropical Grassland Society of Australia.
9. E. Teller, 'Widespread after-effects of nuclear war', *Nature* 310, 621–24 (1984).
10. M. Harwell, *The human and environmental consequences*

of nuclear war (Springer-Verlag, Berlin, Heidelberg, New York: 1984).

11. M. M. Caldwell, 'Plant responses to solar ultraviolet radiation', in, *Encyclopedia of plant physiology*, pp. 169–97.[6/5]

12. S. D. Flint and M. M. Caldwell, 'Partial inhibition of in vitro pollen germination by simulated solar ultraviolet-B radiation', *Ecology* 65, 792–5 (1984).

13. Royal Society of Canada Report, p. 40.[1/7]

14. P. R. Ehrlich et al., 'The long-term biological consequences of nuclear war'.[1/3]

7. The Human Cost

1. D. Pimentel, 'The impact of nuclear war on agricultural production', in Harwell, *The human and environmental consequences of nuclear war.*[6/10]

2. D. Campbell, *War plan UK* (Granada, London: 1983).

3. D. Campbell, p. 293.[7/2]

4. Food and Agriculture Organization of the United Nations, *1981 FAO production yearbook*, vol. 35 (FAO, Rome: 1982).

5. Unpublished paper by Robert Stuart presented at a SCOPE meeting about agriculture and nuclear war (January 1985, University of Essex, Colchester, UK).

6. *The medical effects of nuclear war.*[2/1]

7. A. Katz, *Economic and social consequences of nuclear attacks on the United States* (Report to Committee on Banking, Housing, and Urban Affairs, US Senate: 1979).

8. TTAPS, 1983.[1/2]

9. I. E. Coggle and P. J. Lindop, 'Medical consequences of radiation following a global nuclear war', *Ambio* 11, 106–113 (1982).

10. W. S. Osburn, Jr, 'Radioecology', in, *Arctic and alpine environments*, eds J. D. Ives and R. G. Barry (Methuen, London: 1974), pp. 875–903.

11. H. L. Abrams and W. E. von Raenel, 'Medical problems of survivors of nuclear war', *New England Journal of Medicine* 305, 1226–1232, (1981). Excerpted by permission of H. L. Abrams

12. *The medical effects of nuclear war*, p. 101.[2/1]
13. Y. Laulan, 'Economic consequences: back to the dark ages', *Ambio* XI (nos. 2–3), 149–152, (1982).

8. Policy Implications

1. H. Kahn, *On thermonuclear war*, (Oxford University Press, London: 1960).
2. H. Kahn, p. 145.[8/1]
3. H. Kahn, p. 150.[8/1]
4. Royal Society of Canada Report, pp. 5 and 7.[1/7]
5. C. Sagan, 'Nuclear war and climatic catastrophe: some policy implications', *Foreign Affairs*, Winter 1983/84, pp. 257–92. © Carl Sagan, 1984.
6. G. F. Kennan, 'A modest proposal', pp. 390–5 and N. Gayler, 'How to break the momentum of the nuclear arms race', pp. 396–403, both in B. H. Weston (ed), *Toward nuclear disarmament and global security*, (Westview Press, Boulder, Colorado: 1984).

Index

Would nuclear war, even of a 'limited' type, devastate the climate of the Earth? For a quarter of a century, debates about the possible effects of nuclear war were carried on in ignorance of their full implications. It was only in 1982 that scientists stumbled on a new line of research which has since shown that nuclear war could bring about catastrophic changes in the climate – the nuclear winter. For the first time, the possibility of human extinction could not be excluded. The risk of nuclear winter gives a new dimension to the nuclear debate.

This book clearly explains the new research and explores the implications arising from it. The authors, two physical scientists and a biologist, have wide experience in presenting the material to the general public.

The book analyses how a nuclear war might be fought and how smoke and dust from fires and the explosions could make much of the Earth cold and dark. It shows how this would devastate plant and animal life, destroy harvests and leave most of the Earth's population ill and starving. Unless there is a nuclear war, there is no sure way of knowing whether the nuclear winter theory is correct. So the evidence and uncertainties are fully discussed.

Moral and political issues are explored, altering the character of the choice between nuclear deterrence and disarmament. The threat of nuclear winter is horrific. Yet it could provide new hope if its implications are properly comprehended.